INTIMATE SKETCHES
FROM BIRD LIFE

By the same Authors

THE ART OF BIRD PHOTOGRAPHY
BIRDS OF THE DAY

THE KINGFISHER

A colour photograph enlarged from
16 mm. Kodachrome cine film

Pl. 1

Intimate Sketches from Bird Life

Written and illustrated
by
ERIC J. HOSKING, F.R.P.S., M.B.O.U.
AND
CYRIL W. NEWBERRY, B.Sc., F.R.P.S.

with an introduction by
JULIAN S. HUXLEY, M.A., D.Sc., F.R.S.

COUNTRY LIFE LTD.
2–10 TAVISTOCK STREET, COVENT GARDEN
LONDON, W.C.2

FIRST PUBLISHED . . . 1940
REPRINTED 1943
REPRINTED 1945

THIS BOOK IS PRODUCED IN
COMPLETE CONFORMITY WITH THE
AUTHORISED ECONOMY STANDARDS

PRINTED IN GREAT BRITAIN
BY JARROLD AND SONS, LTD., THE EMPIRE PRESS, NORWICH

INTRODUCTION

Mr. Hosking and Mr. Newberry have given us an admirable sample of British bird life. Mr. Hosking is, of course, one of the most enterprising and successful of our bird-photographers, and the pictures here reproduced are well up to the standards we have learnt to expect from him. In particular I commend the series which documents the life of that strange bird, the Stone Curlew, at some of its most intimate moments. Those of the Little Owl, as well as being fine examples of flashlight work, also fulfil the same function of documentation. In this case they conclusively demonstrate that the Little Owl feeds mainly upon insects and earthworms, and is not normally a killer of small birds, whether game chicks or songbirds. This had, of course, been amply proved on a very large scale by the inquiry instituted by the British Trust for Ornithology, but those who were convinced beforehand of the guilt of this "foreigner" have continued to attack the Trust's findings so that the evidence of Mr. Hosking's camera is very welcome.

Many others of the pictures are very beautiful—I personally was especially attracted by those of the Partridge and the Grey Wagtail; and from the technical point of view Mr. Hosking has scored a notable success with that notoriously difficult subject, the Wood Pigeon—or rather the wood pigeon in rural surroundings, for our fat London pigeons have learnt more confiding habits.

The method adopted in the text is well calculated to interest the lay reader. The authors have recorded their own observations in considerable detail, thus giving their readers the impression of sharing their experiences and giving a feeling of personal intimacy with the birds and their lives. We cannot do without the more usual method of standard description, but this has frequently been given by others, and our authors provide a new type of approach.

From their descriptions I carry away some vivid pictures of unfamiliar scenes of bird life, which can be revealed only to patient watching. There is the change of instinct in the

partridge just before the eggs are due to hatch, when the
hen bird stays on the eggs for much longer periods and
with shorter breaks: the wonderful picture of the cock
partridge wild with excitement when the hen brought him
back to the nest to show him the newly-hatched chicks: the
strange instinct of these same chicks to make for their father
to be brooded, and the way the parents call their surprised
chicks away from the nest into the safety of the underbrush,
almost as soon as their plumage has dried.

With the stone curlew, there is the fascinating story of
the ritual of nest-relief, when the relieving bird offers its
mate a stone before taking its place on the nest. This
presentation of nest material at the moment of changing
places is common among birds which share the duties of
incubation. I myself have seen it among herons and egrets,
where the rite is still more highly developed, the material
(in this case a stick) being offered and accepted to the
accompaniment of elaborate raising of crest and aigrette
plumes, flapping of wings, and loud exciting calls. In still
other cases, the nest material is offered as a part of courtship,
away from the nest. This is so in the great crested grebe,
where both sexes exchange beaksful of wood, and in Adelie
Penguins, where, according to Dr. Levick, the offering is
made only by the cock to the hen.

A very interesting record is that of the male stone curlew
carrying off the young under his wing, often yards at a time.

With those beautiful creatures, the Grey Wagtails, our
authors record the frequent bringing in of fish to the young
—a curious trait in an insectivorous bird. However, many
birds are adaptable enough in the way of food. A friend
of mine who owned a trout farm found a wren busily
engaged in picking out young fry at the yolk-sac stage from
their troughs in an old mill, and carrying them off to
give her fledglings. It is through such adaptability that
evolutionary change often begins. What starts as individual
adjustment may become reinforced by mutations affecting
instinct, which are then incorporated into the hereditary
stock-in-trade of the species. This is the principle of
organic selection, enunciated by Mark Baldwin and by
Lloyd Morgan, by which the inheritance of acquired
characters (in this case new habits) is simulated. Actually,

of course, no such inheritance occurs, the acquired character holding the fort, so to speak, until mutation and selection step in under its cover and alter the animal's heredity.

The description of the buzzard's routine at the nest is calculated to impress on those unfamiliar with bird life that strange tendency to a strict and detailed ritual which characterises so many of the actions of birds. And the fact that jays and magpies stop their mobbing attacks on birds of prey as soon as these latter reach their nests will give the student of animal behaviour food for thought.

The theoretical discussions and reflections are hardly up to the level of the observations and the photographs; but the chapter on The Approach to Bird-Photography should be very useful in persuading amateurs to take up this exacting but fascinating pursuit.

I commend this book to all those who love nature, take pleasure in accurate and sympathetic record and appreciate high technical excellence in bird-photography.

JULIAN S. HUXLEY

FOREWORD

IT is a curious fact about our civilisation that, while the population tends more and more to be attracted to the large towns, and the industrial machine seems ever to extend its hold on us, there is at the same time an increasing appreciation of country life; a deeper understanding of its problems as well as of its delights. Never has there been a greater interest in the preservation of our national heritage, and never before have we been so concerned for the beauty that surrounds us. The threat of industry and commerce has aroused the realisation that we must not regard natural beauty with indifference, and partly as a result of this there has been a shifting of our attention in our leisure hours to the manifold pleasures and interests of the countryside. This tendency has been reflected in the number of books on nature subjects which have been published recently, and in the prominence given to these topics in the daily Press under such headlines as, "Nature is News," and while almost all aspects of country life have had their share in this attention, bird life seems to have captured the imagination in a special manner of its own.

Most of us are interested in, and notice birds to some extent, though our methods of so doing may be widely at variance. Perhaps it is the power of flight that is one of the greatest attractions in a bird, for we are all aware of the fascination of a flock of gulls wheeling about the stern of a ship, or breasting with outspread wings the rising air currents over the cliff edge. It may be the agility of the little blue-tit as he clings and turns on the nut suspended outside the window, or the perkiness of the friendly-looking robin that waits on us as we dig in the garden, but whatever is the individual feature that attracts our attention, most of us watch birds solely for the pleasure and recreation that the watching affords. The casual glance leaves a slight impression with us and we are pleased. That is all. It arouses no conscious mental process—no urge to enquire into the birds' lives.

Although this state of affairs holds with a considerable

majority of people, there is a minority, and happily an increasing one, who see in bird life more than a mere item of decoration or entertainment in Nature's pageant, and more than a vaguely useful cog in Nature's machine. They see a gateway to the study of biological science, to the understanding of life itself.

Between these two extremes there are all shades of attitude to bird-watching. There is a multitude representing all ranks and professions who (and we must now differentiate between "watching" and mere "seeing") watch and study bird life primarily as a result of their love of birds. They get enjoyment, and rightly so, from avian company, but at the same time display an intelligent appreciation of what they are seeing. The extent to which the scientific outlook asserts itself controls the development of their studies, but there is, in general, a mental recording of fact and, to varying degrees, a self-questioning, a striving to understand the motives underlying the actions observed. It is for such persons that we have written this book.

We have attempted to record some of our observations in such a way that the pleasure we have experienced in the field and in the hide may be passed on to the reader, but at the same time the facts have been presented as accurately as possible, so that they may be of value to others as well as to ourselves, and may serve as a basis for a consideration of some of the interesting problems that occur to the intelligent watcher of bird life. Experiences among birds and accounts of bird behaviour can be very interesting in themselves, but the significance of birds is of greater interest still, and one of our aims is to encourage an appreciation of the value of ornithology as a factor in the study of evolution and the understanding of the mystery of life.

To further this end we have adopted a particular plan in the book. The first part is devoted to an account of observations on a number of birds. We have described just those things we saw, commenting on incidents which may perhaps seem trivial, as well as on those of unusual importance. There has been no attempt to compile a complete record of the birds mentioned, but rather to present a number of intimate sketches from their lives. To make these details more comprehensible to those who are perhaps not very familiar with the objects of our studies, we have inserted at the beginning of each of these chapters a short description of the birds mentioned, with a few general notes on their main characteristic features.

A later chapter has been devoted to a consideration of some of the problems that have occurred to us in the course of our observations, but for obvious reasons, we have tried not to be dogmatic. A great deal concerning the lives of birds is still unknown and many of their actions and the circumstances governing them are matters for conjecture. We know that birds are individuals and show variations of manner just as men do, and it would be rash for any man to lay down hard and fast general laws as a result of limited observations. Everything that is seen and accurately recorded is of value in adding to the sum of knowledge, but in a science such as ornithology, where deductions must often be based on the notes and records of a number of independent observers, we must proceed with considerable caution to distinguish between reliable and unreliable data. New observations may confirm old ones or they may reveal differences in the behaviour or appearance between birds of a species, and from a true consideration of the observed facts may come new knowledge of the forces controlling bird life, and through that, life in general. To take but one example; there is still considerable mystery surrounding the vast migratory movements of birds. We know that migration does not result from a mere nomadic urge. There is more in it than that. It is an ordered cyclic movement and we have many known instances of individual birds returning to nest in the same places year after year although they have probably travelled some thousands of miles between each nesting season. Various theories have been advanced to explain these regular movements of birds, but none is yet complete, and many more observations of the passage and winter activities of the migrants must be made, and then need to be correlated, before the problem can be completely solved; and migration is but one of the aspects of bird life which, when properly understood, should confirm and perhaps amplify the knowledge of life derived by the biologist in his laboratory. While migration is perhaps one of the major problems confronting the ornithologist, it is too vast a subject to be discussed within the scheme of this book and we have limited our discussion chapter to those problems which lend themselves to restricted treatment, and which can be easily pursued further by study of bird life in almost any garden or by the wayside. Our treatment admittedly touches only the fringes of the problems, but it is a beginning on which the reader can build and develop his own ideas.

In a final brief section we have tried to give an insight into our methods of watching and photographing wild birds. It would, of course, require a whole book to explain everything in detail, but we feel that many of our readers will be interested to have a summary in the present volume, and some perhaps will be stimulated to extend their studies.

This foreword would be incomplete without a mention of our indebtedness to the numerous friends by whose assistance and encouragement our studies have been made possible and this book has come into existence. It is impossible to mention them all by name, and in some cases, for obvious reasons, it is undesirable to do so, but we recall with gratitude the extreme kindnesses we have received at the hands of the owners of the estates on which we have worked, and the help that has been given us by bailiffs, keepers, wardens and others. To the Editor of *Country Life* we express our thanks for permission to use considerable extracts of text and numerous photographs which have appeared in that journal, and our appreciation of his assistance in the preparation of this book, and we acknowledge to *The Times, News Chronicle, Daily Mail* and several periodicals, the encouragement we have received from their use of many of the photographs included in this volume. Some there are sure to be, who feel that they have been forgotten, but let them rest assured that they are gratefully remembered and only the limits of this book prevent an adequate expression here of our appreciation of the many friends we have made through bird-watching.

CONTENTS

ILLUSTRATIONS

Chapter I

THE ENGLISH PARTRIDGE

Description:

For general build, see photographs (Plates 2 & 5).

Length about 12 inches, but wings short in proportion.

Colour essentially greyish, but marked with fine streaks and bars of black, brown and chestnut.

Nests on ground, chiefly in sheltered positions round borders of cultivated land.

Found over most of England and Wales in suitable localities. Most common in East Anglia.

ONE of the most intriguing features of bird-watching is the scope it affords for making new discoveries. There is a thrill in seeing something for the first time, a lure in the unfolding of the unexpected, and there is so much yet to be learned about bird behaviour, that, if we want new experiences, if we want to see incidents that have seldom, if ever, been recorded before, we do not need to go to wild and inaccessible places in search of rare birds, but we can satisfy our ambitions almost from our own doorsteps.

Most of us, whether we live in town or country, are to some extent acquainted with the partridge. We know it by name and associate it with shooting. From time to time we see it in the poulterers' shops and on the table, and we regard it as a fairly common bird. Indeed, its breeding range extends over the greater part of the lowlands of England and Wales. In September each year it achieves front page news value and yet in spite of this, or perhaps because of this, it is, in general, extremely shy and few people have seen or even read of the events that take place at the nest.

For this reason then, we are devoting our first chapter to an account of some observations made during the hatching of a family of partridges. The shyness of these birds makes many landowners and gamekeepers unwilling to allow observation and photography at the nest, for, especially in the early stages of incubation, the hen partridge will desert her eggs on the slightest provocation, but we were fortunate in meeting a gentleman who readily gave us permission to work on his estate in East Anglia, and instructed his game-keeper to assist as far as possible. During the season over one hundred nests were found, but surprisingly few of them could have been photographed without extensive clearing of the undergrowth, and this we wanted to avoid as much as possible.

The nest selected as the subject of our photographic work was at the base of an old oak tree to which a wire fence was secured. The lower strand of wire passed only a few inches above the nest itself, but this drawback was more than offset by the comparative clearness of the ground. We had watched the bird make the shallow scraping in the ground which was to serve as her nest, and had observed that one egg was laid early each morning until the full clutch of thirteen was complete. It is worth mentioning at this point that the weather at the time was warm and dry and that this may have influenced to some extent the rate of egg production, as on another occasion we have noted as few as seven eggs laid in fourteen days. In fifteen nests that were kept under regular observation, the average number of eggs was twelve.

We realised the need for not disturbing the sitting bird and the importance of making only gradual changes in her surroundings, so having selected a nest, we waited until the hen had been brooding for ten days before any work was started. The hide was first erected some twenty yards from the nest, on the verge of a field of oats, and was left for two days so that the cock and hen partridge would become perfectly accustomed to it, after which it was moved up a little at a time, when the hen was off to feed. We soon discovered that she went to feed at the same time each day and brooded for four and a half hours at a stretch, so we knew that if she was off at 8.0 a.m., she would probably remain at the nest until about 12.30 p.m. Later observations showed that this was the case not only with this particular bird, but with many other partridges, and that these times were altered only if rain or other unforeseen occurrences interfered with the birds.

On the twentieth day of incubation the hide was in position, five feet from the nest, but photography was not started until the eggs were "sprung." This condition, which develops some twenty-four hours before hatching, is detected by rubbing the eggs together, when they make a noise like the crumpling of brown paper. It was for this sound that we were waiting, in the knowledge that the partridge would then be far more attached to her eggs than at any other time. We noticed at this period that her feeding times altered, and she stayed brooding for as long as eight hours without a break. When she did leave the nest it was for only ten minutes, whereas earlier absences had lasted for twenty-five to thirty-five minutes.

In conference with the gamekeeper, we estimated that the eggs would start to chip at four o'clock one afternoon and that probably they would all hatch during the night. This would mean that the chicks would leave the nest as soon as the sun was warm enough next morning. Accordingly, the hide was occupied before breakfast with the intention of photographing the family as they left the nest together, but a first glance showed that the cock bird was not to be seen. At all the other nests we had watched during the hatch, it was noticed that the cock came and sat by the side of the hen and that he helped to warm and dry the chicks, and it was concluded that the chicks in this nest had not yet hatched. The only thing to do of course was to wait and see what happened, and after three hours had passed, the hen suddenly got off the nest and hurried away. From the hide, none of the eggs appeared to have hatched, but a closer examination showed that they were all chipped and that one of the babes was pushing his way out. This was photographed, and the hide re-entered with little delay, as the idea suddenly dawned that the hen must have gone to find the cock and tell him that the chicks were hatching. There was no time to spare, and soon there was a sound of running in the oats at the back of the hide. The hen came first, closely followed by the cock. Without any hesitation they approached the nest, and there followed as fascinating and amusing a scene as anyone could hope to witness. The cock, peeping into the nest, saw his first-born, and went wild with excitement. He rushed frantically about the place, banged himself against the old oak, and came back to the nest for another peep as though he could not believe his own eyes. Seven times he came back to convince himself that the eggs were really hatching, and meanwhile the hen stood to one side and looked on proudly. After the cock's excitement had worn off a little, the hen settled down to brood again, but he, still very restless, continued to walk round and round the oak trunk.

These events all took place in what seemed a very short thirty-five minutes, between 9.40 and 10.15 a.m. Once hatching had started, the babes quickly followed each other, and by 10.40 a.m. at least four were hatched. The hen continually pushed her head under her body and appeared to help the babes out, and it is of interest to note that she then pushed the top half of the eggshell into the bottom half. By 11.0 a.m. all the brood seemed to be hatched, and the hen called in a low voice to the cock who had been preening himself only a yard from her. He came and sat by her side, and at 12.10 p.m. one of the young ones was strong enough to push himself out from under his mother, and to stagger across to the sheltering warmth of his father. A few minutes later there came, from under the hen, another fluffy body, still quite wet, and he followed his elder brother and disappeared under the cock.

Shortly afterwards, the cock was disturbed by the passage of another family of partridges in the nearby oats, and, subservient to the territorial instinct rather than to domestic duty, he got up suddenly and hurried into the oats to drive away the intruders. There was not much of a fight, but just a brief shuffling of wings and the trespassers flew off while their babies appeared to run as best they could, obviously being too young to fly. At the nest under observation, the young ones that had been sheltering under the cock prior to this disturbance, seemed very surprised at their father's sudden disappearance and hurried back to shelter under their mother's warm body. The cock, however, soon returned and the babes were seen to push their way over to him once more. Although it was only a few inches, this seemed rather a long journey for them as they stopped every inch and seemed to be out of breath. It was surprising, though, how quickly these youngsters gained

Hen partridge returning to brood after absence for feeding

Pl. 2

The first egg hatched at 9.40 a.m.

The hen called in a low voice and the cock came to her side

Pl. 3

At 12.10 p.m. one of the chicks was strong enough to push himself out

The cock, sitting near the hen, helped to dry the chicks

Pl. 4

At 1.35 p.m. the hen led her babies from the nest

Pl. 5

their strength, for by 1.0 p.m. they were walking about quite strongly although they did not venture more than a few inches from their parents.

Apart from the adventures of the babies, which were quite amusing to watch, very little happened until 1.33 p.m., when the cock suddenly jumped up and half flew and half flapped his way along the ground. We are convinced that he was not disturbed from the hide as no noise or movement had been made for some little while. He alighted about twenty yards away and then came running back to the nest. Here he called ever so softly and the hen got off the nest. She, too, began to call very softly and, slowly following the cock, walked away through the undergrowth. The babies seemed rather amazed at this and squeaked to their parents to come back. This invitation to leave the nest for a larger world was more than the chicks could understand, so both cock and hen returned to try again, and this time there took place one of the most delightful incidents we have ever seen. The cock made a way, ever so slowly, through the undergrowth, then came the hen, and she was followed by her family of thirteen fluffy, dappled chicks. What a sight this was, and what an opportunity for a cine-camera! The young were very weak on their legs and continually fell over, but their parents allowed for this and kept calling encouragingly and coaxing them until they had all gone out of sight behind the tree. This first journey at so young an age may seem rather surprising, but our experiences suggest that, if the weather conditions are favourable, partridge chicks leave the nest only a few hours after hatching in order to be free from the fleas and lice which almost invariably infest the nest. The journey is, however, quite short, usually only the matter of a few yards and then the hen continues brooding the young until they are stronger and ready for food. In bad weather conditions, such as continuous rain, we have known a family of partridges to remain on the nest for as much as twenty-four hours after hatching.

And so we left the partridge family to gain strength, and, as we vacated the hide, we could not help wishing them the best of luck in the fast-approaching shooting season.

Chapter 2

THE WOOD PIGEON

Description:

The general build of this bird is clearly shown in the photograph (Plate 6).

Length about 16 inches.

Colour—bluish grey on the head and back, with glossy green and purple patches on the back of the neck and a conspicuous white collar patch at each side. The wings and tail are dark greyish-brown, the former with narrow white edges to some of the feathers, and a well-defined white bar on each wing is prominent during flight. Nests usually in trees in woodlands, but not infrequently it breeds in the parks in large towns.

Found over almost the whole of the British Isles.

THE wood pigeon, as its name suggests, is a bird of the woodlands and copses, but strangely enough, it is by no means confined to such places, and, in company with other pigeons, it inhabits some of our towns and cities. The squares of London are favourite haunts of the bird, and it finds many a roosting place on the ledges and niches of the massive stone buildings. The Londoner looks on the pigeon as a familiar and friendly bird. He likes to watch it strutting the broadwalks with tail spread and chest expanded, and he encourages it with tasty morsels; and the wood pigeon responds readily to him. It has thrived and multiplied in the company of man to such an extent that some flocks, such as in Trafalgar Square and at St. Paul's, have achieved considerable fame and attract more than a few sightseers at all seasons of the year.

This must make strange reading for the country dweller who knows little of the town, for he, too, is familiar with the wood pigeon, but finds it different in the extreme from the bird described above. He knows it as a shy bird, suspicious and distrustful of man, and difficult to approach, except by stealth.

This effect of environment in producing such striking differences between birds of the same species, is, in some respects, rather surprising, for birds as a rule are credited with very little intelligence. If we allow them some reasoning power, then the variation of habit is easy to understand, for while the town wood pigeon is encouraged and protected by man, his country relative is regarded by the farmer and market gardener as a dangerous pest on account of the considerable damage it does to growing crops. The wood pigeon consumes large quantities of wild fruits including beech and hazel nuts and acorns, and holly and ivy berries, but it also enjoys young green shoots, and from the growers' point of view pays too much attention to peas and beans and to potato, turnip and other root crops. As a result of this tendency it is much persecuted, and in many places is shot at whenever it comes within range of the gun.

If, however, we deny the wood pigeon the ability to distinguish between safe and unsafe association with man, how are we to explain the known facts about its behaviour? The two distinct characters shown by different wood pigeons may have resulted gradually from a process of evolution, a natural selection of breeding stock by the elimination of those birds which were slowest to adapt themselves to their surroundings. Thus, in the country, there is the greatest survival of those pigeons which have an instinctive fear of man, and a corresponding reduction in numbers of those that venture too near his gun; while in the town those pigeons which have most quickly taken advantage of man's hospitality have stood the best chance of survival, and from them has sprung a race which shows a considerable trust in man.

Whatever may be the true explanation of this dual character of the wood pigeon, the feature makes it a fascinating bird in either its urban or rural habitat, and observations at a nest in a situation little frequented by man proved so full of interest that they are worth relating. The nest was in the fork of a hazel, about fifteen feet above the ground, and although the position was somewhat difficult from the photographic point of view, it was the most readily accessible of the nests that we had found. Past experience had taught us something of the probable shyness of our quarry, so preparations for photography were made with considerable care, and no serious work was attempted until the eggs had hatched and the young pigeons were several days old. A hide was then constructed. It consisted of four upright poles supporting a square platform at the required height, and this was enclosed with walls and a roof of hessian. The work was done, little at a time, each evening, when the fading light tended to mask the altered appearance of the pigeons' outlook. It took a week to finish, but the slow progress was justified at once by the pigeons' disregard of the structure, and then later by the series of photographs we were able to obtain.

By the time our preparations were complete, the young pigeons were fairly well developed and the old birds were leaving them for considerable periods while feeding and collecting food. We took the opportunity to enter the hide during one of these absences of the old birds, and having adjusted the cameras, settled down to watch and to wait. The babes seemed to be asleep in the bottom of the nest and there was very little going on, when suddenly, after about an hour's waiting, we heard a crash of wings in the hazel, and the hen alighted between the hide and the nest. We "froze" in whatever attitude we were in at the time and scarcely dared to breathe, she was so close to us, but she was in no hurry, and leisurely looking around and taking stock of things, she seemed determined to keep us in suspense.

Presently she jumped the remaining distance on to the side of the nest and for ten whole minutes, that seemed like as many hours to us, she remained perched there, but then she flew to a branch just above the nest and settled down quietly with her back to the hide. This relieved us of the tension to some extent, but the period of waiting seemed interminable. She seemed unready to feed the chicks, probably because she was waiting for the food in her crop to soften, and the chicks, strange to say, showed no anxiety to be fed. They lay quietly in the bottom of the nest. After twenty minutes of this expectant waiting, the old pigeon flew down suddenly to the side of the nest again, and this time she began to moan. She went into a series of convulsions and appeared to be in dreadful agony. The chicks

The wood pigeon perched close by the nest

The hen flew to the side of the nest again and this time she began to moan

Pl. 6

The chicks pushed their beaks into and down the throat of their mother, and all three moved up and down with a bowing motion

Pl. 7   *The chicks and their mother at the upper limit of the bowing motion*

The hen puffed out her breast feathers to cover the chicks

Pl. 8

The same feeding procedure was maintained during the growth of the chicks

Pl. 9

understood this procedure perfectly, and half standing, one on each side of their mother, they pushed their beaks into and down her throat and all three moved up and down with a bowing motion. The hen regurgitated the food for three periods lasting seven, five and three minutes, with only a brief pause between each, and although the meal had thus lasted for a quarter of an hour, the chicks were not at all satisfied and clamoured loudly for more. They tried again and again to push their beaks into their mother's throat, but the attempts gradually weakened as they became sleepy, and finally they sought shelter and sleep under their mother's breast. At first, however, they met with little success because she was still perched on the side of the nest, but with difficulty, and suffering, it seemed, from exhaustion, she wobbled her way further across the nest, and the chicks were able, in ostrich fashion, to bury their heads under her and go to sleep.

The hen, too, tried to sleep, but she only dozed fitfully, and was alert for every little unusual sound, lifting her head as if to ascertain the cause. She was further disturbed by a shower of rain which began to fall at this time, and she did her best to cover the chicks by puffing out her breast feathers to their fullest extent, but the attempt was only partially successful, and soon she and they were bejewelled with large, shining beads of water. Her next act, when the rain had stopped, was to give the chicks a clean by stroking their backs a few times with her beak. This seemed a totally inadequate toilet, but it satisfied her maternal instincts and shortly afterwards she left the nest. Her departure was as sudden as her arrival, and with a few noisy strokes of the wings she was out of sight. The chicks remained quiet and still at the bottom of the nest, and as at the end of another hour there was no sign of either of the parents, and the light was fast fading, we took our leave.

Several other visits were paid to the nest during the growth of the chicks and a similar procedure was observed each time, but as the young pigeons became stronger and more feathered, the caution and nervousness of the parent birds seemed to increase, and they spent less time at the nest with the chicks. The preparatory waiting period at the nest before the feed diminished to nothing, although, of course, there may have been a time for softening the food before the old bird's arrival at the nest, and the meal itself was completed in one continuous period lasting about seven minutes. At the end of the feed, the old birds would fly quickly away, and we could only feel that in spite of all our preparations and attention to detail, the pigeons, when relieved of some of the exacting demands of their family, were somewhat distrustful of the hide, and it strengthened our belief that the wood pigeon of the wild places is one of the most difficult subjects to approach that the bird-watcher can find in these islands.

Chapter 3

THE STONE CURLEW

Description:

For general build see photograph (Plate 10).

Length about 16 inches.

Colour—sandy, flecked with dark brown; the underparts lighter.

The large yellow eye is a striking feature.

Nests on ground, usually on sandy heath land, well away from marginal hedges.

Found chiefly in southern and eastern England from April to October.

A few winter in this country in the south, but the majority migrate abroad.

It is crepuscular, feeding at dusk and by moonlight.

BY contrast with the birds we have so far considered, the stone curlew is quite unknown to many people. It is, for the most part, a summer visitor to these shores, arriving here usually in April and nesting locally on open heath land. The bird is considerably smaller than the common curlew and has not the characteristic long bill of that species, but in the matter of build and general colouring, the two are not greatly dissimilar, although the smaller bird is rather lighter.

We found the stone curlew a fascinating bird to watch, both on account of its manner and because of the uncertainty among ornithologists concerning some of its habits. It literally compelled our attention for days on end, and the periods of our observations extended through many weeks and covered several seasons. One of the first stone curlews that we selected for detailed study was nesting on an open sandy heath in East Suffolk. It proved to be of especial interest because on one leg it wore a ring, by means of which it was subsequently identified as a bird that had hatched the previous year from a nest on an adjoining heath. Our interest was still further increased when, the following year, we were able to observe the same bird again, nesting so near its previous site that, had our hide been left standing all through the winter, we could have photographed both nests from the one position; and this in spite of the fact that the stone curlew had probably wintered abroad, perhaps in North Africa, and had travelled many hundreds of miles between the nesting seasons.

The nest was quite typical of the stone curlew, and consisted of a slight scrape on the ground well away from the margins of the heath. Only a sparse and wiry grass, and a few stems of ragwort, seemed able to eke an existence on this porous ground, and the nest was devoid of practically all shelter, but as is not unusual in the case of the stone curlew, there had been some attempt at furnishing it with a few dry rabbit droppings.

Our first visit to the nest had been during the period of incubation, and the bird had shown herself to be very shy. We had approached by way of a depression in the ground, so that we were about one hundred yards from the sitting bird when our heads came in her view, but although we moved very cautiously, we saw her leave the nest at once and walk quickly and stealthily away. After a little distance her walk broke into a run and this in turn gave way to a low fugitive flight which carried her just clear of a distant hedge and so out of our sight. Accordingly, we laid careful plans for the erection of a hide. On account of the openness of the situation and the lack of shelter, a low dummy structure was erected first of all at a distance of about fifty yards from the nest. In the fading light of successive evenings, the structure was moved gradually closer to the nest, as was done in the case of the partridge, but to avoid an overshadowing effect the stone curlew hide was kept as low as possible consistent with reasonable comfort for the occupants. It may be of interest to note that in general, even with many ground-nesting birds, we have found that a tall hide, up to about six feet, seems to have no appreciable effect on the bird, and such a height is of considerable value from the point of view of comfort and ventilation during protracted periods of observation. It needs little imagination to visualise the interior of a small, closed tent exposed for hours to the pitiless scorching of a summer sun, and when

The stone curlews change over. The hen arrives to relieve the cock   Pl. 10

The cock about to leave

The hen comes on

Pl. 11

The hen settling on the eggs while the cock moves away

The cock at the nest restores a displaced egg

Pl. 12

*The cock helping the chick
out of its shell*

*The cock with re-
mains of the egg from
which the first chick
emerged*

Pl. 13 *The change-over after the first egg had hatched*

countless small flies and insects buzz unceasingly within, the misery of the occupant is almost complete if his head must be close to the roof.

But to return to our stone curlew hide; this was kept down to a height of about four and a half feet, as even this seemed tall in such an open situation, and it was finally erected about six feet from the nest. Again our preparations appear to have been adequate, as on the very first occasion when the hide was occupied, one of the parent birds returned in less than half an hour and settled unconcernedly on the eggs. Our first near view of the stone curlew was unforgettable. In the manner of plovers in general, she alighted on the ground at some little distance from the nest, and approached it in stages by a zigzag route, pausing at intervals and turning her head on one side in what we might almost call an attitude of enquiry. Her curiosity satisfied, she proceeded again for a few yards, and so her advance continued. We could not help noticing what seemed at first to be a peculiar stoop in her walk, but what we subsequently found to be quite a frequent characteristic of the stone curlew, and that is the inclination to walk with the neck stretched forward and the head held low, for this attitude accentuates more than ever the fascination of her large yellow eye. Apart from the eye, and a light bar on the wing, the stone curlew is not striking in its colouring and, indeed, for good reason, for it relies on its protective coloration to escape notice; but the bird is by no means dull in appearance, for it is neatly flecked with dark brown on a sandy-coloured base and the underparts are considerably lighter even to the extent of being cream-coloured.

In making a series of photographs of this bird, we found that although at first she had seemed so shy, she very quickly became accustomed to unusual sounds. The first few clicks of the shutter caused her to lift her head and listen, but soon she ignored the shutter, and even the sound of changing plates seemed not to trouble her, so we made an experiment to determine to what extent an unusual noise could be increased without causing her alarm. From the occasional clicking of the camera shutter, the disturbance was increased by tapping a metal plate holder against a tripod leg. The bird showed no interest or concern at all, and we resorted to clapping; still she appeared not even to hear it, and we increased the range and volume of sounds by shouting and whistling, but she sat steadfast and unperturbed through it all. It is of interest to note, however, that when, as a final test, we very slowly pushed the corner of a handkerchief out of the peep-hole in the front of the hide, she immediately became alarmed and left the nest before half an inch of the handkerchief was protruding, and stood watching the hide suspiciously from a distance of about twenty yards.

The following year we were fortunate in finding a nest on 1st May when it contained only one egg; we were, therefore, able to keep the stone curlew under observation for the whole of the brooding period, although photography and close study were restricted to the last week before hatching, as we considered it inadvisable to erect the hide during the early stages of incubation when the bird was less strongly attached to her eggs. The second egg was laid early on 2nd May, and brooding began at once, so, as we expected the incubation period to be twenty-three days, we planned to begin the erection of the hide about the 17th or 18th of the month. Work proceeded much the same as in the previous year, but when we were ready and anxious to place the hide in its final position close to the nest, the weather was unsettled and stormy, with a terrific wind blowing across the heath, and we had in consequence to make the hide even lower than before and to peg it down, and weight it with large stones. The securing of a hide in windy weather is always something of a problem, for many birds, as we had demonstrated with the stone curlew, will not tolerate an unusual movement near the nest; and to practically all of them a loose and flapping hide is a source of annoyance and an object of suspicion.

The completed hide looked a sturdy little structure, but as we looked back at it after making our final adjustments, we could not help thinking of the cramped and possibly tormented hours that might be in store for us in our quest of the stone curlew.

We left the hide for two days after it was completed, in order that the birds should accustom themselves to it without any additional alarm, and close observation was not begun until a few days before the hatch was expected. The birds showed complete confidence right from the beginning of our study, and only a few minutes after the hide was first occupied, one of them was seen hurrying through the short heath land grass. He came straight to the nest and settled down to brood without showing any fear or suspicion of our presence. After a short while he was heard to call softly, and we saw his mate running through the short grass towards the nest. On arrival, she stood by the side of the brooding cock, who slowly got up, and bowing, offered her a small stone. She accepted it from him and then settled down on the eggs, while he, very slowly and sedately, walked away to what proved to be an observation point not many yards from the nest.

Less than an hour had passed when the cock, from his observation post, gave a low, soft whistle quite unlike the loud, weird call that these birds frequently utter when on the wing at night. His call was answered by the hen who was still brooding, and he came back to the nest. This time it was she who offered him the stone, but in a manner quite unworthy of his sex, he refused the offering, so the hen carefully replaced it between the two eggs. She rose to her feet, bowed, and with a crouching walk, hurried from the nest. In all we witnessed fifteen of these changes at the nest and much the same thing took place each time. The ceremony of the stone seemed to have some special significance to the birds and was seldom omitted. We were unable to arrive at any precise interpretation of its meaning, but it undoubtedly was associated with the expression of emotional feeling, and it was inspiring to watch.

During the first period of five hours' observation from the hide, five changes were witnessed, and only once did the brooding bird leave the nest until the other was standing by. On following days the changes were not nearly so frequent, and we assume that the short periods of brooding were due to the wind, which was still very strong, making the brooding bird uncomfortable and in need of relief. In spite of the strong wind, the two birds kept up a continuous conversation and we were able, after a time, to understand partly what it meant. Thus, a short whistle seemed to indicate that all was well and that the brooding bird was not ready to leave, while a series of low whistles by the non-brooding bird meant that it was coming to take over brooding. After the new bird was brooding it would give a whistle on a higher note and then its mate would retire to the observation point.

An incident that provided us with some amusement, but at the same time with a good deal of interest, occurred once when the hen was leaving the nest. She accidentally moved one of the eggs out of position and it was some time before the cock was able to restore it to its proper place. First he tried to brood only one egg, but he seemed disturbed in mind about this, so got up and walked in circles round the nest, trying in various ways to restore the displaced egg, until eventually he succeeded in hooking it back with his beak.

On the evening of 23rd May, it was noticed that one of the eggs had "sprung" and we presumed that it would hatch in about 48 hours' time, that was, during the afternoon of the 25th. Accordingly, we entered the hide directly after lunch on the 25th, prepared to stay until the eggs did hatch. During the afternoon a further incident revealed to us the stone curlew in a new light. A black, rough-haired retriever came bounding across the heath, and the team-work of the pair of birds was as perfect as if they had been drilled to such an emergency. The hen, who was at the usual observation point, was the first to notice the dog, and ran towards it. The dog immediately gave chase, while the hen, feigning partial disablement, fluttered along the ground and drew it away from the nest. Right away across the heath she took it and then just sprang into the air, circled round and came back. All the cock did was to get up from the eggs and walk away a few yards to the back of the hide. On returning, the hen whistled to him from near the observation point, and he returned to the eggs. We stayed in the hide until it was quite dark, but still the eggs had not hatched and we feared that in spite of our efforts we should miss the most interesting period of all.

During eight hours spent inside the hide during that afternoon and evening, we only saw the change-over twice. It may have been because of the approaching hatch, or perhaps because the wind had dropped, but the birds were content to spend much longer periods of brooding. Soon

The cock returning to brood the two chicks (one dry; the other still wet)

The cock whistled softly while brooding the chicks

Pl. 14

The last change-over before the chicks left the nest

In stages they went farther and farther from the nest

Pl. 15

after the first change the hen flew right away out of sight. On returning, she called from a distance and was immediately answered by the brooding cock, and we then heard, at close quarters, the loud, weird call of this bird from which it probably gets its name of "curlew." During the call the beak was opened wide, but the head was not raised as it frequently is in the case of, say, the redshank or the gulls.

Early next morning we visited the nest to see how the young chicks were progressing, but found to our surprise that they were still not hatched. The eggs were chipped to a considerable extent, and one of them had a hole almost a quarter of an inch in diameter in the top. As the chicks could be heard whistling inside their shells, it was almost certain that they would hatch during the morning, so with renewed enthusiasm we entered the hide and waited for the old birds to return. There was not long to wait before the cock was seen hurrying back to the nest. He took much longer than before to settle down over the eggs and whistled almost continuously to the unhatched chicks. At 10.7 a.m. he pushed his head under his body, and we actually saw him take the top of the shell off one of the chicks. The incident, natural enough in itself perhaps, was fascinating to behold, and we experienced one of those thrills which come from time to time to the bird-watcher—or, indeed, to anyone—on the threshold of a discovery. We do not pretend to be the first to have seen this action of the stone curlew, but the incident was new to us and was a rich reward for the hours of watching devoted to this bird. Having removed the piece of shell, he held it in his beak, and continued to brood for about a quarter of an hour. He then walked a little way from the nest, stamped on the piece of shell until it was crushed, and swallowed the pieces. Returning to the nest, he brooded again for a short while and then carried away the larger piece of shell and crushed and ate that in the same manner. While he was doing this, the hen hurried up to the nest and settled down to brood the egg and the wet chick, but in less than half an hour the cock was back and waited for the hen to leave. It is rather remarkable that from the time the first egg chipped to the time it hatched, was not less than sixty-one hours.

3

The second egg hatched at 11.43 a.m., or one hour, thirty-six minutes, after the first. The cock helped the chick out as before, but instead of brooding the two chicks, he hurried away immediately with the small piece of shell. The hen came on the nest and brooded the young ones, but she seemed ill at ease, and before long went away with the large piece of shell, which she ate in the same manner as the cock had done.

One chick was very soon dry and it crawled up between the body and wing of the cock, who was then brooding, and the second chick followed suit as soon as it was strong enough. In the next three hours we saw two further changes of duty at the nest. On one occasion, the cock, when leaving, walked towards the hide with one of the chicks still under his wing, and the babe dropped to the ground midway between the hide and the nest. The hen brooded the remaining chick, but at the same time called to the other, who, after expending much energy, staggered back to her. At 3.30 p.m. the cock, who was then on the nest, got up and slowly walked away, carrying one chick under each wing. Whether this was by design or accident it is hard to say, but about three yards from the nest he settled down to brood them again. The chicks now went for short walks on their own. A few inches seemed a long way for them, but it must be remembered that one was only four, and the other five and a half, hours old. Twenty minutes later, they made another move, and so in stages they went further and further from the nest. The cock carried them each time, but we noticed that when he did drop a chick, he did not come back to fetch it, but called it after he had settled down to brood the other. By 5 o'clock they were out of sight in the thicker growth of the heath, and as we emerged from the hide after the ten-hour vigil, we saw both old birds run swiftly along the ground in their characteristic crouched fashion, and finally take to the wing.

It will have been noticed that, in the course of this description, we have distinguished between the cock and the hen stone curlew, and readers may have wondered on what grounds we have determined the sexes, for there is very little difference between the plumage of the adult birds. Our decision was based on the fact that, in each of the pairs that we have observed at close quarters, we have noted one bird to be slightly larger than the other, and by comparison with museum specimens, we have assumed the larger bird to be the cock. Unfortunately we have seen no emotional display that would have confirmed our assumption, but if we are correct, then it is of interest to note that it is the cock bird that takes the greater share of domestic duty, especially in the later stages of incubation.

Whether stone curlews are double-brooded or not is a point that we have been unable to decide, but we are inclined to the belief that sometimes, at least, they are. On a number of occasions we have seen their eggs in September, and it seems unlikely that more than an isolated pair would have been unsuccessful till so late in the season in rearing a first brood. It is reported that a certain number of stone curlews winter in this country, especially in the south-west, and it seems not unreasonable to suppose that many of these may be second-brood birds that have scarcely acquired sufficient strength to make the longer journey. Time and a good deal of patient work are still required to elucidate many of the outstanding problems concerning the stone curlew, and we look forward to further opportunities of watching it.

Chapter 4
THE LITTLE OWL

Description:

A typical small predatory bird, as may be seen in the photographs (Plates 17 & 19).

Length about 9 inches.

Colour generally dark greyish-brown, but flecked with white.

Nests in holes in trees and buildings, and not infrequently in disused rabbit holes.

The bird is really a native of the Continent, but was introduced into this country in the latter part of last century. It is now found in most parts of England, except the few northern counties, and in Wales.

WHEN Shakespeare wrote, "Some have greatness thrust upon them," he can little have foreseen its application to the subject of this chapter, and yet, if greatness can be measured in terms of public attention, the little owl can surely be classed as "great" among our avifauna. Few birds have, in a short space of time, made so many enemies, and yet, it is to be hoped, so many friends.

Since its introduction to this country from the Continent, towards the close of last century, the bird has steadily extended its range, and wherever it has appeared, so farmers and landowners seem to have classed it as undesirable. It has been accused of many misdeeds, the most serious of which are, undoubtedly, its alleged attacks on game and poultry chicks, but it is significant that many of the charges against it are past history and savour more of rumour than of substantiated fact; and rumour, we all know, can spread rapidly.

It may be that in the early days of its spread among us, in the course of adjusting its numbers and distribution, that it did, of dire necessity, enlarge the range of its diet occasionally at the expense of farmers and game preservers. With the spread of the bird there was, of course, a spread

The hide erected at the little owl nest under the slates of a derelict building

Pl. 16

One of the little owls brings a cockchafer to the nest in the building. (This, and the little owl photographs, were taken at night by flashlight)

Pl. 17

of interest in it, and it seems probable that its points of conflict with man were its most readily remembered, and most oft repeated, characteristics. Certainly it acquired an unenviable reputation, and there were some people who went so far as to call for the extermination of the species as a British resident.

The little owl was not, however, without friends, and many careful and reliable observers were of the opinion that the species was of considerable economic value to the farmer and agriculturalist, and it was in an endeavour to find the true representative facts that the British Trust for Ornithology undertook, in 1936–37, an investigation into the feeding habits of the little owl. It is doubtful whether there has ever been a more thorough investigation of any feature of bird life, for the observations represented eighty-seven different localities covering thirty-seven counties in England and Wales. Nearly 2,500 food castings, each of which probably represented about a day's food, were carefully analysed, as well as the contents of a number of nests, and the results indicate, as conclusively as is possible in the study of anything so variable as a bird, that the little owl has a restricted and definite normal diet which is composed chiefly of small rodents, and of insects such as beetles, earwigs and daddy-long-legs.

The report of the enquiry (*Report of the Little Owl Food Enquiry*—A. Hibbert-Ware) makes interesting reading, and at the same time exhibits a scientific impartiality which should disarm any serious criticism of its findings, but it has been our experience that many of the persons most directly concerned by the presence of the little owl will not be convinced by the printed word, or by any amount of statistics. We know that in bird life there are exceptions to almost every rule, and that there have been, undoubtedly, occasional instances of little owls attacking game chicks, but this fact makes little excuse for those who, in ignorance or in defiance of the findings of the Trust, and often on the basis of unreliable information, still maintain and help to spread the belief that the little owl should be suppressed.

It was then, in the hope that photographic illustrations might reach further than the printed word, that we determined, during the nesting season of 1938, to secure a number

of photographs which should show the little owl in the act
of carrying food. We were, at the time, working in Wales,
in a locality where game chicks, though not abundant, were
not scarce, and where small birds of many kinds were to
be found in plenty, so that the district may be taken as
offering sufficient opportunity to the little owl to select its
fancy in the way of food.

The first nest was found on 17th April, when, strolling
across a field, we noticed a little owl fly out from a thick
hazel bush, to be followed by an excited flock of small
birds. We made a search of the likely nesting sites in the
vicinity and eventually discovered the nest in a small, derelict
stone building which served to shelter sheep in rough
weather. The roof timbers were for the most part rotten,
but at one end a few slates remained intact, and under the
shelter of these the little owl had its nest on top of the
substantial stone wall. We were first led to the spot by
the discovery of a pellet, and then, after lifting a number
of slates, we saw the hen little owl still sitting tight on the
nest. It seemed unwise to disturb her, so we withdrew
with the intention of returning later, but although we made
several visits, it was a full week before we found her away
from the nest, and discovered that she was brooding only
two eggs.

From time to time when we were in the neighbourhood,
we went across to see the progress of the little owls, but
every time we found the hen sitting and did not like to put
her off. On 28th May we noticed that she was sitting a
good deal higher in the nest than before and concluded that
she must now be brooding small chicks, so two days later,
finding her still on the nest, we took the risk of lifting her
up, and found two chicks about ten days old. She allowed
us to do this without protest, and when we put her back
she just tucked the chicks under her and complacently
settled to brood them again.

The construction of a hide was begun on 3rd June, but
for various reasons we were unable to begin detailed observations until 11th June, by which time the chicks were
about three weeks old. Our general observations of this
bird led us to the conclusion that although it is not infrequently seen about during daylight, it seldom feeds before

dusk, so accordingly, we made our principal studies in the evening, usually between about 9.0 p.m. and 1.0 a.m., a period which, at this time of the year, covered the last half-hour or so of daylight and extended well into the full darkness of night.

As we entered the field in which the old building is situated, one of the owls began to call from a nearby tree. It was a weird note, sounding rather like a sharp, high-pitched, "kee-ow, kee-ow," which grew in its excitement as we approached the hide. The flashlight apparatus, which had, of course, to be used for the photography of this bird, was quickly erected, and as our assistant made his departure, so the cries of the little owl ceased, and we settled to our studies in the peaceful quiet of a fine summer's evening. We had not been waiting long, when one of the owls came down and perched on the slates in front of us, and ran the few feet down to the nest entrance. The light was still fairly good for observation, and we had a grand view of him as he stood momentarily before going in to the chicks. The hooked beak, typical of the predatory species, held a cockchafer in its unyielding grip, and the general mien of the bird was one of scowling ferocity.

When our observations were resumed, three days later, there was the same excited calling as there had been on previous occasions when we approached the nest, but the old birds lapsed into silence as soon as our escort left the vicinity of the hide. The period of feeding activity began about 9.40 p.m., a few minutes after we had heard the first beetle fly by the hide with a loud buzzing noise, and the visits to the nest were then very frequent, the interval being about two or three minutes. For a short while, it was possible to see, though not very clearly, the food brought by the owls, and it appeared to consist chiefly of cockchafers, with occasional moths, but the fading light soon made visual observation unreliable and we had to depend on the photographs for the record of what was brought. After the first burst of activity, the visits to the nest became much less frequent, but feeding was still in progress when we left the hide at 11.10 p.m.

The following evening we again watched this same pair of owls, beginning our observations at 9.15 p.m. The first beetle was heard in flight at 9.35 p.m. and ten minutes later the first visit was paid to the nest when one of the parent owls returned with a cockchafer. At this, the chicks, who had been quiet during their parents' absence, began calling with a kind of snoring noise not unlike that made by young barn owls. They raised themselves up to greet their parents, and could, at times, be seen in the entrance of the nest. Owing to the difficulty of changing flash bulbs, it was not possible to expose on the owls every time they returned to the nest, but during this spell of watching we took seven photographs, the majority of which show them with food in their beaks.

As with many other species that we watched during the 1938 season, our observations on the little owls were several times interfered with by the adverse weather conditions, but although we were not able to obtain any further photographs of this pair of birds, we noticed that the young were still in the hole on 19th June, but had left by the following evening. On that occasion, the old birds again called "kee-ow" at us from a nearby tree, but we were unable to find any trace of the young, although we believed them to be somewhere about the old building. On 5th July when we returned to dismantle the hide, the little owls were still about, indicating that these birds are, at least for some time after nesting, very restricted in their wanderings.

During the same period as that covered by the observations just described, we were able to observe two other pairs of little owls, both of which were nesting in rabbit holes, as is not unusual in this part of the country. The two nests were within two hundred yards of each other, but we worked principally at one of them as it offered the better photographic possibilities.

It was on 7th May that we saw a little owl perched on a branch, close against the trunk, of an oak tree, and while we watched, it was joined by another, but although we suspected a nest in the vicinity we failed to find it at that time. Later, however, we returned to watch these birds, and soon discovered the rabbit hole which they were using for a nest. The hole went straight into a bank for a distance of about five feet and then turned, and the nest was apparently beyond the bend, as we were unable to see any sign

Little owl leaving the nest in rabbit-hole

Pl. 18

The only unidentified food. It is thought to be a rain-soaked earthworm

A cockchafer is being carried to the owlets

Pl. 19

This time the food was an earthworm

Yellow underwing moths were included in the diet Pl. 20

Cockchafer was the predominant food

Pl. 21

of it from the entrance. On 14th May, and again on the 15th, we sat in the car and watched the vicinity of the hole from a distance of about fifty yards, but we saw only one bird and concluded that the other must have been brooding, although we did not see the cock take any food to the hole. Much the same was noted during observations on the 23rd and 31st May and on 1st June, but on 3rd June, some little while before dusk, we saw one of the owls fly out from the hole and make a short circuit, alighting in turn on several ant-hills in the vicinity. It may have been feeding, although from our viewpoint we could not be sure of this, and after a short time it returned to the hole. We saw more activity at the hole on 5th June, but again could not see if food was being carried, so two days later we erected a small hide near the nesting hole.

On 8th June we made our first observations from this hide, commencing our vigil at 8.0 p.m. During the remaining period of daylight we saw no activity on the part of the owls, but numerous rabbits kept us entertained by their antics within a few yards of the hide. At 9.55 p.m. we had our first thrill, for two eyes, glowing green in the semidarkness, stared at us from the hole. Their effect was almost hypnotic, but as we fired the flash for a photograph, they disappeared, and the bird scampered back down the hole. A quarter of an hour later, the other bird flew down from above and went directly into the hole without stopping. As he did so, he made the most uncanny whistle, not unlike that of the barn owl but even, it seemed, more eerie. He stayed only a moment in the hole and then came running out, but before flying, he hesitated just long enough at the entrance for us to fire another flash.

Several more times that evening we were aware of activity at the hole, but the night was so dark that we had to judge what was taking place by the impressions of ghostly forms moving in front of us and by the occasional slight scratching sounds made by claws on the tree and on the ground. In the case of birds like the owls, whose every movement is so silent, there is often considerable difficulty in anticipating their return in the dark, and we found that we had to be very much on the alert to get good records of the birds returning with food, especially as the youngsters, at this stage, seemed to be silent, and gave us no clue to their parents' movements.

We visited the hide on the 9th, and again on the 14th, when things happened very much the same as before, but this time when the hen first looked out at us, we remained quiet and let her go without making an exposure. On this occasion, we heard the first beetle at 9.57 p.m., and we noted that the first visit to the nest with food was made six minutes later. It was too dark to see the food clearly, but it was certainly some kind of beetle, and we wondered why the feeding of the little owl corresponded so closely with the time when the beetles were in flight. As far as we could make out, the little owls did not take them on the wing, and we came to the conclusion that they must watch the beetles settle after flight and then capture them. Once the beetles were settled on their food they would be very difficult to distinguish, and this fact probably accounted for the slowing down of the owls' feeding after the first burst of activity. One feature that interested us was that this pair of owls was nesting on considerably higher ground than the pair in the old building, with the result that darkness set in rather later in this case, and this had the effect of delaying the flight of the beetles by about a quarter of an hour and making a corresponding difference in the period of activity of the owls.

We made a number of further observations during the next fortnight, and each time as we developed our negatives we found similar results. The diet of these pairs appeared to be entirely insectivorous, with beetles and moths as the chief items. We saw no evidence of ants in the photographic records, nor indeed, would such food be likely to show on account of its small size, but it may be that these insects are included in the diet of the little owl since, on occasions during daylight and once during an evening watch from the hide, we saw the birds deliberately alight on and peck at the ant-hills in the vicinity of the nest.

On 2nd July, we had our first view of one of the owlets. Just as dusk was falling, it appeared at the mouth of the hole and looked straight at the hide in a most comical way. It twisted its head to one side and then the other, and blinked as if it could scarcely believe its own eyes and then, presumably out of respect for the photographer, kept bowing till we could scarcely restrain ourselves from laughing. The chick was still fluffy, but, with its down puffed out, appeared almost as large as the adults, and we were surprised not to have seen it earlier, as the nesting hole was practically level and presented no difficulty to the chick's movement. The chick was, in fact, by now quite agile, and when a car came along the nearby road, it turned and bolted down the hole and we saw no more of it that evening.

The first visit of the adult birds on this occasion was at 10.5 p.m., when a yellow underwing moth was brought to the nest. We squeaked softly at the bird as it reached the mouth of the hole and it turned to face us while we fired a flash, but it was by now accustomed to the "artificial lightning" and proceeded straightway to feed the chicks, and left the nest a few seconds later. Another visit, probably by the other bird, was paid at 10.25 p.m., but by that time it was too dark to see what food was brought, and we relied on our photograph, which subsequently showed it to be a cockchafer. Several more visits were made during this spell of watching, and we noticed that at this stage of their development the chicks were much more noisy than they had been earlier. They heard their parents' approach long before we did, and welcomed them with a wheezy, snoring kind of noise. We were glad of this, for it eased considerably the strain of prolonged, intense watching.

During a short spell of watching the following afternoon, we saw no sign of the parent birds, but once again we saw a chick appear at the mouth of the hole and perform much the same antics as we had previously seen. Owing to the inaccessibility of the nest itself, we had little idea of the age of these chicks, but, believing them to be nearly ready to leave the nest, we decided to spend as much time as possible with the little owls. In consequence, we returned to the hide that evening and focused the camera on a stake which we had driven into the ground near the nesting hole, and we were fortunate in securing several photographs of the parent owls perched on the stake before they dropped down to the hole.

The weather was very unsettled and stormy for a few

days after this, but the following evening, 4th July, we took
the opportunity, during a break in the deluge, to visit the
little owl hide, arriving at 9.45 p.m. We noticed one of the
birds flying in the neighbourhood as we approached, but
during an hour's vigil we saw no sign of activity at the nest,
neither did we hear any sounds from the owlets. It is perhaps noteworthy that on this occasion, although we listened
carefully, we did not hear a single beetle in flight, and we
associated the slowness of the feeding at this period with
the inactivity of the beetles, and probably, also, of the
moths. At 10.45 p.m. rain began to fall heavily again, so
we hastily made our departure from a field already partly
water-logged. Similar conditions prevailed again the next
day, and after an hour's watching without a sight of the
little owls, we were driven from the hide at 9.30 p.m. by
a severe thunderstorm.

The 6th July continued the downpour that was having
its effect, not only on the little owls, but on wild life of all
kinds, but by the middle of the evening the sky cleared
somewhat and gave promise of a few hours' respite, so we
made our way once more to the nest in the rabbit hole.
We kept a close watch for the appearance of beetles and
moths and heard the first beetle in flight at 9.55 p.m., but
it was a solitary one and we heard no others during the rest
of our stay that evening. At 10.5 p.m. one of the owlets
made a brief appearance at the front of the hole as if to
usher in another feeding time, and five minutes later one
of the parents came down with what appeared to be a grub
or a worm quite two inches long. It disappeared quickly
into the hole before we had a chance to photograph it, but
in the course of that evening we did manage to get two
photographs and we found that the food in the beak consisted of earthworms in each case.

The final observations were made from this hide on
8th July when, since we already had a good collection of
photographs of the owl at the nest hole, we chose to focus
the camera on the stake. Although not raining, the weather
was still cloudy and dull, but beetles were heard on the
wing at 9.50 p.m. There was at first little activity at the
hole, but at 10.20 p.m., hearing a movement outside the
hide, we peered in its direction and saw what, in the dull

A violet ground beetle was the prey

Pl. 22

At dusk one of the owlets appeared at the mouth of the hole

Pl. 23

light, we took to be a rabbit. The object came nearer till it stood by the nest hole, and then cursing our luck that we should have focused on the stake, we saw it to be one of the little owl chicks returning from a walk. At this moment, one of the parents flew down and fed the owlet at the mouth of the hole, but we dare not, of course, move the camera for fear of disturbing them. Having been fed, the chick disappeared down the hole, and the adult then flew away, and in their absence, hoping that the feed might be repeated, we pointed the camera towards the hole, but though we waited till close on midnight, and though we saw the chicks again, we failed to get the photograph that would have made a fitting end to our series.

Summarising our observations on the feeding activities of the little owl, we find that at the nest in the old building we made twenty-seven flashlight exposures, twenty-one of which show food in the beak. In every instance it is a cockchafer. In the case of the other nest described, we were able to take forty-two photographs, thirty-three of these show the little owl with food, the list of which is as follows:

22 cockchafers; 2 earthworms; 4 yellow underwing moths; 1 violet ground beetle; 3 dor beetles; and 1 unidentified prey.

It will be noticed that our observations confirm the insectivorous diet mentioned in the report of the Enquiry, and emphasise the predominance of cockchafers, but it is perhaps striking that we recorded no instance of rodents being taken for food. It may have been that rodents were scarce in the immediate vicinity of the nests we were watching, and if so, this would account for their absence from the owls' diet, for, in our experience, these birds hunt over a very restricted area. Each nest that we have seen has been in a tree, or has been situated under, or nearly under, a large tree, which has served as a perch from which the owls have watched, and subsequently caught, a large part of their food, and while this has not been used exclusively, it is very rarely, during the nesting period and for some time after, that we have been unable to find the little owl in its immediate neighbourhood.

In conclusion, it is of interest to recall the finding of the Forestry Commission that the larva of the cockchafer is one of the greatest menaces to the roots of young trees, and if for that reason alone, the little owl, as one of the greatest enemies of the cockchafer, deserves considerate treatment at the hands of landowners and agriculturists; but all this only emphasises the findings of the Trust, and it is unnecessary for us to use further argument in defence of the little owl. We leave our photographs to tell their story.

Chapter 5

THE GREY WAGTAIL

Description:

For general build see photograph (Plate 24).

Length about 7½ inches.

Colour—head and back slate grey with definite whitish eye-stripe. Breast and underparts yellowish. White outer tail feathers are a prominent feature.

Nests usually on sheltered ledge of wall or bank, close to running water.

Found during the breeding season in most parts of the British Isles where suitable hill streams provide nesting sites. In winter may often be found on lowland waters and by the coast.

"The Grey Wagtail," a sombre title indeed! Yet how misleading to those who do not know the bird that forms the subject of this chapter, for his name sadly belies him, and he is the very spirit of vivacity and charm. A lover of the fast-flowing brook, his tempo is attuned to his environment, and his plumage, if it does not vie with Joseph's coat in its range of colours, does attract attention by its simple smartness.

How delighted we were then to find this bird comparatively numerous in the district in Central Wales where we made our headquarters. Every brook seemed to have a pair nesting along its banks, and it was a great surprise to us to find no less than six nests in a walk of about one mile. In addition to these nests by the brookside, we came across several in quite different situations, so it may be of some interest to recount a few of our observations.

The first nest was thoroughly typical of the bird. A tumbling mountain stream splashed its way down a small gully in the hillside. Its rugged banks were for the most part steep and in places were overhung by eaves of turf interwoven with the roots of the shrubs that grew in the ravine. Just under such a roof the grey wagtail had built

its nest on a small ledge in the bank, some three feet above
the level of the brook. The exterior of the nest was constructed of grass and root fibres, while the lining was of
grey and white cow hair. On the 23rd of April, when it
was first noticed, there were four light-greyish eggs,
speckled with darker grey and fawn and having several
brown hair-lines on the larger ends. Incubation had
started, and when we saw the nest on the 2nd of May, all
the eggs had hatched and we estimated the chicks to be one
day old.

A hide was erected on the rocky bed of the brook and
the wagtails quickly showed their disregard of the structure
by using it as a perch, but before we could begin any
photography it was necessary to admit considerably more
light to the nest, and a piece of the overhanging bank was
carefully removed. This improved the conditions enor-
mously without in any way distressing the birds, and almost
at once we were rewarded with some of the most charming
sights that it has been our good fortune to see. The colouring of both birds was exquisite, the first impression being
of immaculate grey and gold, while their dainty vivacious
manner produced a thrill that will not quickly be forgotten.
The cock was a fine bird with dark-grey head and back, a
black eye and dark-brown bill, and whitish eye- and cheek-
stripes. His throat was black, the breast and underparts
yellow, and the wings and tail were brownish-black with
white edging to some of the feathers. The hen was generally
similar, but the colours were rather more subdued; the most
noticeable difference between the sexes being that whereas
the cock had a black throat, that of the hen was whitish and
slightly mottled with grey.

We spent several periods in the hide, observing the
family of wagtails from the 2nd till the 13th of May. Both
parent birds were busy feeding the chicks. They hurried
about and seemed never still for a moment, and even when
they were at the nest feeding, their tails scarcely stopped
wagging up and down. Feeding intervals were very short,
but as in the case of most of the insectivorous-eating birds,
there was now and again a much longer interval of some
twenty minutes, during which it is presumed that the
parents went away together and fed themselves. On several

The hen grey wagtail at the nest by the brook

The dipper brought as many as three minnows at a time,
carrying them across the bill

Pl. 24

The nest against the wall of the tool-shed

The cock at the nest on the hillside

Pl. 25

occasions both cock and hen were at the nest together, and it was noticed that the hen did not show the usual signs of emotion that the smaller birds usually do when the hen is in the presence of the cock. Once we saw the cock feed the hen while she was brooding the chicks.

Both birds showed a fondness for the brook, and strutted about on the stones and paddled in the water in search of food, and, to our surprise, frequently returned with small fish. Insects formed the major part of the diet, but long-winged flies, with their wings still intact, were given to the young. Gnats were a favourite, and it is interesting to relate that whereas the cock collected quite a number before flying back to the nest, the hen brought them back one at a time. They were also feeding on several kinds of larvæ, including, we believe, those of the dragonfly, but these could not be identified with certainty. We took particular note of the fish course, as we had not noticed this item referred to in the accounts of other observers. Twice in five minutes the hen brought back what we took to be minnows. One was brought at a time and carefully turned so that the chick could swallow it head first, but even so there was considerable difficulty in getting it down and for quite a time the tail was protruding from the chick's mouth.

It is interesting to note that the wagtails' nest was only a few yards from the nest of a dipper, and from the hide we could watch the dippers as well. These birds were also bringing minnows to the nest and we noticed a difference of manner in that they often brought as many as three at a time, carrying them across the bill, and, whereas the wagtails collected a large part of their food from close to the nest, the dippers usually flew away down the brook to the river.

The second nest of the grey wagtail was interesting because of its situation in ivy growing on the wall of a tool shed. It was some eight feet from the ground, and was at least fifty yards from the nearest brook. It was first shown to us on the 16th June when it contained four eggs. These hatched on the 21st. A wooden hide had to be erected to this nest, and the work was done a little at a time and then left for two days before observations began on the 28th June. We quickly noticed that only the hen was feeding the chicks, and she wore a very bedraggled appearance as if she had been nearly worn out with rearing earlier broods. Most of the beauty of her feathers was missing, and she had none of those fine, clear-cut colours that so characterise the grey wagtail. This bird, too, brought a considerable amount of fish to feed the young, and owing to the lateness of the season, the fish were distinctly larger than those we had seen at the other nest. Again the tails protruded from the chicks' mouths for some minutes as if the chicks were trying to digest the heads before swallowing the rest. Crustaceans, caterpillars and small moths, were included in the food brought by this wagtail, but fish was the chief item during our observations. The diet did not seem to agree with the chicks, for, one by one, three of them died, and the fourth seemed to be very weak when it did eventually leave the nest.

The third and last nesting site we shall describe was, in its turn, quite different from the other two, and was particularly unusual for the grey wagtail. By the side of an old farm road high up the hillside was an outcrop of rock, overgrown in the course of generations with a tangle of mosses, ferns and grasses, and in the bank so formed, was the wagtails' nest. It was found on the 16th of June, when, as in each other case, there were four eggs. A hide was erected, but owing to adverse weather conditions it was only possible to fit in two periods of observation—on the 1st and 3rd of July—and the young were well advanced at the time. Both birds were soon seen with food, and the hen returned first, alighting some three feet below the nest and climbing the remaining distance up the bank to feed the hungry chicks. In this case the tangle of foliage surrounding the nest prevented her, to a certain extent, from wagging her tail continuously as the other birds had done.

Shortly afterwards the cock returned, and his procedure was very much like that of his mate. He walked up to the nest from below, but appeared to be much more nervous.

The food brought by these birds was, of course, modified to some extent by their surroundings. There was no fish, since they were a long way from the nearest brook, but the staple food seemed to consist of moths and greenish caterpillars, and there were a few light-brown grubs on occasion.

The feeding intervals were quite short, but every half to three-quarters of an hour the old birds went off on their own for about twenty minutes, and the young ones either slept or preened and stretched themselves by mounting on the backs of their brothers and flapping wings from that position. They were fine, well-developed youngsters, and would have flown from the nest probably about two days after we left, that is, about the 5th of July.

Before concluding this account of the grey wagtail, we should make it clear that of the three nests we have described, the first is truly typical of the bird and is representative of the majority of the nests we saw, while the second and third descriptions refer to individual examples. The grey wagtail is undoubtedly a bird of the running brook, but in spite of this, there seems to have been little evidence that fish is a regular part of its diet, whereas our observations revealed that two of the three pairs watched were feeding on minnows. We have since noticed in the recently published *Handbook of British Birds*, a reference to the taking of minnows, and we hope to confirm the extent of this feeding habit by a further study of other pairs.

Chapter 6

THE PIED FLYCATCHER

Description:

A good general impression of these little birds can be gained from the photographs (Plates 26 & 31).

Length about $4\frac{1}{2}$ inches.

Colour—the cock is striking in his black and white plumage, but the hen's colouring is more subdued, the blacks being generally replaced by soft greyish browns.

Nests in holes in trees in well-wooded country, and in crevices in masonry, and appears to favour nesting-boxes where these are provided in suitable localities.

Found locally in north and central Wales, and in the extreme north of England.

It was on the 4th of May, when, accompanied by the keeper on an estate in Central Wales, we tramped the wooded valleys and lingered watchfully from time to time in places that seemed likely haunts of the pied flycatcher. Although this bird is not widely distributed in England and Wales, nesting only in the more hilly districts in the west and north, we understood it to be fairly plentiful in the part where we were staying, and we had been watching anxiously for several days for its arrival. Neither we, nor any of the local people with whom we had spoken, had heard or seen any sign of it, although the woods at the time were comparatively leafless and afforded good visibility. It is fairly safe to assume that the birds had not yet arrived back in this locality from their winter quarters, although they were a little overdue.

We were staying at a house set on the fringe of a wood and were accustomed to seeing plenty of wild life almost on our doorstep, but our satisfaction can be imagined when, early the following morning, we saw a pair of pied flycatchers quite close to our bedroom window. This caused us some little surprise, because, according to the observations of T. A. Coward and others, the males arrive some days before the females, but the most astonishing thing was

Cock and hen pied flycatcher on the perch by the nesting-hole

Pl. 26

Spotted flycatcher

Pl. 27

Cock pied flycatcher at nest in crevice of stone wall

Pl. 28

The hen pied flycatcher

Pl. 29

that although these birds must have arrived in the locality during the night and could not have been more than a few hours in these woods, they were already building a nest and were busy carrying large dead oak leaves to their chosen site in a crevice in the stone wall of an outhouse. Even if the sexes arrived separately in this country, we are of the opinion that they arrived together in this, their nesting locality. Our observations led us to ask whether pied flycatchers pair for life, or had they paired during the migratory flight? There could hardly have been the usual courtship and pairing between the time of arrival in this country and the commencement of building, and certainly not after the occupation of a nesting territory by the male.

The distinctive and cheery little song of the cock bird was the first thing to attract our attention as we left the house, and the pair always seemed to be about, feeding on the alder saplings nearby, carrying nesting material, or, in the intervals, sportively flitting between the roof, the surrounding trees and the overhead electric cables.

We watched this pair of flycatchers from their arrival on 5th May until the 13th, when our work was interrupted by an accident while working on a tawny owl.

We were able to return to Wales after a three weeks' absence, and continued the observations on the flycatchers from 7th June until the young ones flew on 20th June. During the building of the nest a branch of a tree was planted in the ground to stand close by the nesting hole and serve as a perch, but no close inspection of the nest was made at this time, neither was photographic work started until 11th June, when the young were several days old. Both birds were fearless and careless of us, going about their business even when we stood close by the nest. The cock was a striking bird, black on the head and back and white on the underparts, but with white patches on the forehead, side of neck and wings, and a white fringe to the tail. He was a plump little fellow and gave the impression of being rather smaller than the more common spotted flycatcher. The hen was generally similar to the cock, but less striking because she was of a soft brown tinge in place of his black and she lacked the white patches on the forehead.

A large part of the food brought to the nest by the pied

flycatchers was collected from the alder saplings growing nearby, but some was gathered from the ground, among nettle banks and undergrowth. It consisted chiefly of grubs and green and brown caterpillars, but a few moths were brought to the nest. There is a marked difference between the habits of the pied and spotted flycatchers in the matter of hunting for food, for the spotted catches a large part of its food on the wing, flying up from some vantage point and returning often to the same perch. We noted, however, that while the pied prefers to hunt chiefly among the trees and undergrowth, he has by no means lost his agility on the wing, and twice we saw him drop a caterpillar just before arriving at the nest, but on each occasion he caught it again before it reached the ground.

During our observations from the hide we saw another cock pied flycatcher flying around, and twice he perched on the twig by the nesting hole. We visualised him as an unmated cock, possibly a young one hatched from this hole last year, who was violating the territorial rights of the pair we were watching, for each time he approached, he was chased from the twig.

At one time we were driven from the hide by a severe thunderstorm, but were able to continue our observations from a window of the house. We noticed that feeding was suspended during the actual period of the storm, and that the hen remained inside the nesting hole, peeping out on occasions as if to see if the rain had stopped. The cock was not seen, and must have taken cover somewhere else.

By the 14th June the young were calling strongly for food, but although the hole was level inside, they did not come to the front to meet the parents as one might have expected, but waited for the parents to go right inside. They finally left the nest, five of them, one after the other, at 9.30 a.m. on the 20th June, and although they were not disturbed in any way—we were watching from a window— they did not return. It was, however, some time before they were out of hearing distance.

We learned during our stay that the same nesting hole had been occupied by pied flycatchers for at least ten years, and while it is not safe to assume that they were always the same birds, it seems likely, in view of the abundance of suitable nesting sites in the locality, that there must have been some continuity and that at least one of the pair had been there before, even if as a nestling. Accordingly, and in view of the unusual procedure we had recorded during their arrival, we determined to make a further study of these birds the following year. Again we saw no sign of them until well after their usual arrival time in some other parts of the country, and we came to the conclusion that the arrival of the migrants is influenced to a marked degree by local conditions. We had previously noticed that, in general, the season seemed comparatively late in this part of Central Wales. The trees were late bursting into leaf, and whereas, around London, the horse-chestnut candles were almost spent by the second week in May, and in the Midlands they were fully open, even in the sheltered valleys of this district the flowers were scarcely developed. The oak and the ash buds showed a similar tendency, although local variations from one tree to another make an exact comparison more difficult in these cases. Among the flowers, bluebells provide a good example, for they were just coming into flower in this district by the middle of May, while in many other parts they were well past their prime.

The time taken by the birds in their journey northward is not in itself the whole answer to the spread of their arrival dates in different localities, for by the kindness of ornithological friends in this district and in Cumberland, we are able to compare the arrival times of the pied flycatcher over a few years, and we notice that the birds were usually seen in the Lake District about seven to ten days before they were seen here. The dates that we have been given are as follows:

Pied flycatcher first seen in:

	Lake District.	*Central Wales.*	
Year		*Male.*	*Female.*
1931	28th April	—	—
1932	27th ,,	—	—
1933	22nd ,,	3rd May	7th May
1934	17th ,,	30th April	6th ,,
1935	22nd ,,	4th May	4th ,,
1936	26th ,,	4th ,,	4th ,,
1937	18th ,,	29th April	5th ,,

The Lake District dates refer to the arrival of the males, and our informant states that the females were generally one to three days later.

More information is needed concerning the movements of the birds between their first arrival in this country and their ultimate arrival in the nesting localities, but whether the majority of them cross the sea together or not, their journey seems to be influenced in some way by the conditions at their destinations. It is difficult to reconcile this fact with the present theories of migration, which suppose not so much an instinctive urge on the part of the bird as a direct stimulus of certain glands under the influence of the changing seasons, but it seems likely that further study of this point may assist in a complete understanding of bird migration.

In 1938 we saw the first pied flycatcher on the 4th May: it was one solitary cock bird and we saw no others. On the 6th, the cocks arrived in force. We saw quite a number, and several local people mentioned to us that they had arrived that day, so we have no reason to suppose that we had missed them earlier. They were singing, though not very vigorously, and we noticed one on the overhead cable by the nest we had watched the previous year. This time he appeared to be alone, although we did see one hen bird in the adjacent wood. The hen was not seen at the crevice in the wall until the 9th May, when she and the cock were both carrying nesting material. This sequence of events corresponds much more closely with that recorded by other observers, and we conclude that unless we were deceived in our observations, the events of the previous year constitute an exceptional case. It is, however, worth mentioning here that in the *Handbook of British Birds* (1938, Vol. I), there is a reference to R. E. Moreau, who records that . . . "migrants passing through Egypt in spring do not flock, but frequently appear to be paired."

We found a number of pied flycatchers nesting in trees. Three of them were in oaks, two of the occupied holes being old nests of green woodpeckers at a considerable height above the ground. A fourth nest was in an alder in a marsh, and two others were in ash trees. One that we photographed was in a silver birch and was of special interest

*At the nest in the silver birch. Note the mud stopping left in the hole
by the nuthatches*

Pl. 30

The pair of pied flycatchers at the nesting-box

Pl. 31

THE PIED FLYCATCHER · 41

in that it was originally the nesting hole of a pair of nut-hatches, and could only have been vacant a short time between the departure of their family and the arrival of the flycatchers. The young nuthatches were certainly in the hole as late as the 26th of May, although they seemed then to be ready for flying, and the hen flycatcher was sitting on eggs on the 14th of June.

Each year a number of nesting boxes in a nearby garden have been tenanted by pied flycatchers, and at one of these we were able to make observations over a limited period. The nest was composed of the same materials as that built in the wall, that is, oak leaves for a foundation and a lining of dead grass. On many occasions both cock and hen arrived at the nest together when feeding the chicks, but he always went in first. She perched either on top of the box or by the side of the entrance, waiting for him to come out, but on emerging he flew directly away without waiting for her.

It is curious that in just one garden, the whole of the available nesting boxes should be occupied by pied fly-catchers. It suggests that the bird is quite common while in actual fact it is far from common in the district as a whole, and it is, of course, practically unknown over the greater part of the British Isles. Such irregular distribution, as well as the irregular arrival from migration, is a feature of bird life which must give us food for thought.

5

Chapter 7

WOODCOCK AND SNIPE

Description:

Woodcock: The general appearance of this stumpy-looking bird is indicated more clearly in the photographs than it could be in words (Plates 32 & 35).

Length about 14 inches.

Colour—the back and wings are marked with successions of ripples of chestnut, fawn, brown, grey and black and the back of the head is heavily barred. The general impression is of a rufous bird. The underparts are distinctly lighter, but still show a marked wavy pattern of fawn and greyish-brown.

Nests on the ground in dry woods and copses.

Found in small numbers locally where bogs and marshland provide suitable feeding grounds, and the right type of nesting site is available in the vicinity.

Snipe: This bird is smaller and of more slender build than the woodcock (Plate 37).

Length about 10 inches.

Colour—dark brown, striped and flecked with fawn, the underparts being considerably lighter.

Nests in long grass, on or near marshland, the nest usually being well concealed.

Found in most suitable localities in the British Isles.

OF all the birds that we have attempted to study and photograph, few have proved more elusive than the snipe and woodcock. These birds are not uncommon in suitable localities and a good deal is known concerning their lives and habits, but photographs of them, and especially of the woodcock, are comparatively few, and so as a matter of interest we include a few in this book. Woodcock, in particular, are a difficult study because, in the first place, their nests are notoriously difficult to find. The birds choose a dry wood with not too much undergrowth, where the ground is thickly covered with dead leaves and twigs to

Woodcock approaching chicks (a flashlight photograph)

Pl. 32

One of the chicks ran to meet the hen as she returned to the nest

After settling on the nest the hen called the chick to her

Pl. 33

The woodcock tucks the chick under her

The bill serves as a prop while she shuffles to a comfortable position

Pl. 34

A favourite perch for the chick was under its parent's bill

The woodcock family about to leave the nest

Pl. 35

form a variegated carpet, and on this they make a nest which is really but a slight scrape in the ground. The marking of the adult woodcock is particularly crisp and clear-cut, and seen at close quarters, the colouring is remarkably brilliant, yet the whole arrangement of bars and flecks forms one of the best examples of camouflage that exists in the bird world, and when sitting on the nest, the woodcock is almost invisible from a distance of a few feet. Whether it is the result of experience, or whether it arises from some natural instinct, is hard to say, but the woodcock seems fully to understand her immunity from observation, and often sits so tightly on her eggs that we may pass unwittingly within a few feet of her, and her only reaction will be to crouch still lower on the nest. The bird whose photographs are reproduced here, was nesting in a larch wood adjoining a busy road. Some clearing was in progress, and woodmen were hauling young larch trees down a ride to leave them stacked near the road for carting. They had already made several journeys, when, dragging a tree rather larger than the rest, they disturbed the woodcock and she flew up, disclosing the nest. It was situated only about six feet from the path the men had been using, yet she had remained brooding until almost brushed off by the tree.

We erected a hide a few yards from the nest and later moved it closer till it was at working distance, but throughout the disturbance the woodcock remained on her eggs. We deferred photography for a few days to let the bird get thoroughly accustomed to the hide, and when we did make a start, we found it quite possible to creep up to the hide, erect the camera and take a number of pictures, and retire, without disturbing her. Seen from a distance of four feet, her colours were really striking. She seemed clothed as it were in successions of ripples of chestnut, fawn, brown, grey and black. The crown of the head was heavily barred with black, alternating with narrow bands of fawn and chestnut, and below this the face was rippled with streaks of fawn and brown. The large dark brown eye was a prominent feature set well back and high in the head, and it was accentuated by a dark brown stripe leading up from the base of the bill.

The woodcock was seldom away from her nest during

the day unless she was disturbed, but on one occasion after she had been put off, we were interested to note her behaviour on her return. We heard her first, walking slowly among the fallen brushwood, but so well did she conceal herself, that we could not see her until she was within a few feet of the nest. She was stepping slowly and carefully to and fro, and peeping again and again through the brushwood with a jerky movement of the head. She worked round the nest in this manner for nearly half an hour, passing at times very close to the hide, and it seemed that she was listening carefully. She appeared to be suspicious and uneasy, but at last she decided that there was nothing to fear and moved quietly to the nest. With her legs straddled across two of the eggs and her breast feathers puffed well out, she lowered herself on to the eggs, but they were not arranged to her satisfaction so she leaned forward, supporting herself on her bill, and shuffled them into position under her. Life seemed very placid for the woodcock, for the woodmen were no longer working in the vicinity, and there was little to disturb the peace of the wood, and she was still contentedly brooding when we left the hide, again without causing her to leave the nest.

We soon discovered that it was the woodcock's habit to leave her nest at dusk to go to feed, so, each evening while she was away, we went along to examine the eggs for signs of chipping. We had, of course, no idea how far advanced the eggs were when they were first discovered, and continual watching gave us the only hope of seeing anything of the hatch. The woodcock is, in general, an early nester, but this bird must either have lost her first clutch of eggs or have been double-brooded, for it was nearly the end of June, the 23rd to be precise, when the first of the eggs showed any sign of cracking. The following evening there was a hole through one egg and a second was well chipped, but the remaining two showed no sign of life.

Fate was somewhat against us in this case, for two of the eggs hatched during that night or very early the next morning, and when we visited the nest before breakfast we found the chicks dry though not yet strong enough to leave the nest. Dark clouds hung low overhead and driving rain was lashing the tree-tops and dripping into the gloom of the wood, and conditions looked hopeless for photography, but with the aid of the flashlight apparatus we managed to obtain a record of the woodcock family. It is a remarkable thing that the modern flash-bulb, which gives a short flash without noise or smoke, has no disturbing effect on many wild birds and animals, who seem to regard it as a natural phenomenon, perhaps akin to lightning. The only difficulty in these cases is the very real one of changing the bulb after it has been used, but this task can be accomplished by the exercise of a little patience and some knowledge of the temperament of the bird being watched. Sometimes the changing of a bulb did slightly disturb the sitting woodcock, and as a hand appeared in front of the hide she would run a yard from the nest, and, jumping into the air, would fly around with her bill pointing directly downwards, her body carried very low and legs dangling. She would then drop into the bracken a few yards away and almost before the bulb-changing was finished she would be back again on the nest.

During the morning the chicks grew stronger, and began to run to meet their mother as she returned, but, although for short periods she sometimes brooded them a few feet from the nest, she kept returning to the two unhatched eggs and at those times called the chicks to her. Once during the morning while the hen was on the nest, there came a sound through the wood as of another woodcock approaching, and we hoped we might see the cock bird join his mate, but although the sounds came quite close, we were never able to catch a glimpse of the bird that made them, and we were able to gather no direct evidence concerning the part played by the cock during the hatching period.

One feature that we had hoped to observe was the method by which the adult woodcock is supposed to carry the young. Most observers are agreed that, when danger threatens, or when the parents are moving on their evening journeys to and from the feeding grounds in the bogs, the young are carried in some manner, but the precise method of carrying is still the subject of controversy. The most generally accepted explanation is that the young woodcock are carried, one at a time, between the thighs of their parents, but although we took every opportunity in the field of watching this particular point, we saw no instance of it and rather came to the conclusion that the practice is less general than is supposed.

There are many features of similarity between the snipe and woodcock, and not the least of these is their general physical resemblance. The snipe is perhaps somewhat less colourful than her cousin, but the marking of light and dark stripes gives her almost equal camouflage among the grasses in which she nests, and she shows the same tendency as the woodcock to sit closely on the nest when disturbed. While on the subject of nests, it is of interest to observe that whereas the woodcock is very conservative in her choice of a site and likes the shelter of a dry wood, the snipe usually builds her nest on open meadow or marshland, and asks only for a tussock of coarse grass to keep the nest clear of the surrounding ooze. This difference possibly accounts, in part, for the more widespread distribution of the snipe than of the woodcock as a nesting species, for both birds, by their manner of feeding, are restricted to localities where bog and marshland abound.

Because of the open nature of the situations in which they nest, and their astonishing confidence in their protective coloration and consequent disregard of a hide and its implications, snipe are usually comparatively easy to study and photograph when once their nests have been located, although it must be admitted that individuals show marked variations in this respect. The pair whose photographs are reproduced here seemed particularly fearless, and it was delightful to watch the co-operation of cock and hen during the period of hatching. The four chicks had emerged from their shells within a short time of each other and the two elder ones were not dry by the time the younger ones had hatched. As soon as they were strong enough to move about a little, the hen got off the nest, walked round a little way and then settled down a foot or so from it. From this position she began to call the chicks, using a soft coaxing note like that used by the partridges under similar circumstances. After a little while the two elder chicks made their way across to her, but the younger ones were still much too weak. It was at this stage that we heard a snipe call from a little distance, and soon saw the cock arrive, but he

A typical snipe's nest

A typical woodcock's nest

Pl. 36

The cock snipe stood behind the brooding hen

Pl. 37

Two of the chicks left the hen and went to the cock

The hen snipe with chicks

Pl. 38

The hen buzzard arrived at the nest bringing with her a rabbit

Pl. 39

was rather more timid than his mate and disliked going right on to the nest. He sat by it for a while and tried to coax the young chicks to him, but finding they were unable to make the journey, he gave up his attempt and flew away. This rather surprised us, but the hen knew how to deal with the situation and returned to the nest to succour her young offspring. Before long the cock put in another appearance and this time took charge of the two elder chicks who by now had wandered a little round the nest. He gathered them together and with his long bill helped them under his breast and settled down to brood them. During the course of the day as the chicks grew in strength, the adult snipes led them by short steps to the shelter of some thick grass a little way from the nest. Neither on this occasion nor on any other have we seen young snipe carried by their parents, but by the following day they had probably been moved from the vicinity of the nest as we failed to put up the old birds or discover any signs of the young ones despite an intensive search over a considerable area.

Chapter 8

THE BUZZARD

Description:

The general build of this bird is shown clearly in the photographs, its predatory character being clearly indicated by the hooked beak (Plates 39 & 43).

Length about 18 inches. Wing span about 3 feet.

Colour—the general impression is of dark chestnut brown, but the feathers are beautifully marked with gradations from fawn to black, and the breast and underparts are considerably lighter.

Nests usually in unfrequented places, in trees or on cliff edges, but persecution has considerably restricted its range and it is now seldom found except in Wales, the West Country, the Lake District and some parts of Scotland.

MORE perhaps than any bird we have mentioned so far, the buzzard captures the imagination and leads the thoughts back to the romantic days when the wild life of this country was less subject to the domination of man than it is at present. In earlier times the buzzard appears to have nested in many parts of the country, but its predatory nature has brought it into conflict with man and its size has made it a conspicuous target for his gun, so that nowadays this beautiful and majestic bird is found only in the wilder and more inaccessible hill districts. One of its strongholds is among the wooded mountain slopes of Wales, but even here its existence is far from secure, and the species is continually threatened. Apart from what we might almost term the legitimate control of the buzzard by landowners and farmers in the protection of their stock, the bird has suffered considerably at the hands of egg collectors, who seem to be particularly active in this part. During the 1938 season, in a search covering an extensive area, we found nine nests of the buzzard, but one after another they fell to the collectors, and to our knowledge not more than six eggs from the whole nine clutches ever had a chance of hatching.

The haunt of the buzzard

Pl. 40

During the meal the cock buzzard arrived at the nest
(Chicks 13 and 11 days old)

Gripping the rabbit under her left foot she began to pull it to pieces
with her beak. (Chicks 17 and 15 days old)

Pl. 41

The first nest that we selected for our detailed observations was robbed after incubation had been in progress for some fourteen days and before we had begun any preparations for our work, but in our second attempt we were more fortunate. The site was quite typical of the buzzard and a brief description of it will assist in establishing the background to the story of the bird.

A narrow, granite-surfaced cart road leads us out of the village where we are staying. Tall hedges fringe it on either side, and brush in at the car windows, as by a tortuous and undulating route we slowly ascend the valley towards the distant hills. We pass a few isolated farms, and then, as we climb, the hedges dwindle, the road becomes more rocky, and we begin to sense the wildness of the place. Presently a grassy track branches from the road and, leaving the car, we climb on foot towards the densely wooded slopes on our right. Below us and to our left we see the road meandering on through the valley. On either side of it is a fringe of pastureland and meadow, with a small group of farm buildings standing out, grey and austere, a reminder that even up here in the solitary places, man struggles to make a living from the soil. Immediately beyond, the bare rugged hills rise steeply to hem in the valley and dominate the view, while high overhead the buzzard glides with motionless wings and draws curves and circles against the sky. The width of the valley is but a stretch of the wing to him, and as we gaze at the pleasant scene, we are impressed with a sense of awe at the vastness of it all and the littleness of man in the face of Nature.

Climbing steeply towards the wood, we pause frequently to recover our breath and at each halt we notice how the view improves when we look back along the way we have come, but our attention is drawn chiefly towards the buzzard who maintains his wheeling flight far above us. Now he circles directly over our heads, watching intently every movement that we make, and then, with a few deft strokes of his wings, sails far across the valley till he is but a small speck against the distant hills. We lose sight of him for a while, but we can be sure he has not lost sight of us, for he is vigilantly guarding his nest in the wood to which we are climbing, and is ready to cry a warning note to his sitting mate the moment we approach too close for his liking. Here we are at the fringe of the wood, and as we turn for a last look back before entering, we see the buzzard close to us. He has appeared as if from nowhere, and dives close over our heads, uttering a sharp, piercing "queeow." In a moment we see the hen bird swooping low above the tree-tops and she keeps up a determined mock attack as we make our way closer to the nest. The ground is very steep now, and we almost need to use our hands to assist us in the last stages of our climb, but as we glance back, we find ourselves looking through the tops of the trees we have just passed, and we reflect, with a feeling of consolation, that the nature of the site will at least facilitate the erection of a hide.

At last we reach the tree that is the home of the buzzard. It is a gnarled old oak, and the nest is situated in one of the higher crutches about fifteen feet from the ground. Three or four small boughs spread upwards and give some shelter to the nest, which is a rather bulky structure, some thirty inches across. Large oak twigs form the foundation, and upon these the nest itself is formed of smaller twigs. Some have been added quite recently and still carry fresh green oak leaves which form a decorative edging. The interior is slightly cupped and is lined and matted with moss or lichen.

This nest was first found by a local boy on the 17th of April, before any eggs had been laid, and we first saw it on the following day when it contained one egg. On that occasion, both cock and hen flew out to meet us as we approached, and kept crying over our heads all the time that we were in the wood. The second egg was laid on the 20th, but apart from periodic visits of inspection, we deferred work at the nest until the eggs had hatched as we did not want to draw attention to their existence for fear of losing them. Accordingly, it was the 25th of May when we first carried some of the hide material to the site. The first chick had just hatched so we did not linger in the vicinity, but hurried away after a brief inspection of the nest. The incubation period was thus thirty-seven days.

It was three days before we were able to revisit the buzzards, and by this time the second egg was hatched.

We stayed about forty minutes on this occasion to begin the construction of our hide, and succeeded in fixing the framework of the platform to the stems of three saplings growing a little above the old oak. An inspection showed that the first food brought to the nest consisted of three young birds and two young rabbits, the remains of which were spread round the edges of the nest. Two days later, on the 30th of May, we worked for another forty-five minutes and fixed wire-netting to form, as it were, a skeleton hide, and covered this with a camouflage of branches and leaves so that it should act as a screen to the hide proper which we intended to erect under the wire-netting. We did this part of the work the following evening, using hessian for the sides and roof, and rough boards for the platform. Again we took the opportunity to examine the nest, and found two fresh rabbits and a field vole. The remaining work on the hide was done a little at a time during succeeding evenings, until on 4th June everything was ready and a dummy lens was fixed in position in the hide. The food brought to the nest during this period had been noted on each occasion, and had consisted very largely of rabbits although a few field voles and three young birds had been included in the diet.

The first attempt at observation from the hide was made on 7th June, when, accompanied by two local boys who had often acted as our trusty assistants, we made the climb to the nesting site. At 2.45 p.m. one of us began the first spell of a vigil that was to last through several weeks, and after the hide was securely fastened and he was comfortably settled with the camera focused on the nest, the remaining three of us made our way noisily through the wood and then completely away from the locality. We saw the buzzard flying high over the valley to watch us take our leave, and we hoped that she had been deceived by our numbers into assuming that no one was left behind.

Although for the sake of convenience and uniformity we use the first person plural throughout this chapter, we should perhaps make it clear that in our observations of this bird, as in most other cases, the hide was occupied by only one of us at a time. Apart from practical considerations of small space in the hide, and the difficulty of arranging for sufficient helpers to see us in and out of the hide at suitable times, we considered it inadvisable to confront the buzzard with more disturbance than necessary, and while we were anxious to obtain as complete a record as possible of her, we did not want to neglect entirely the numerous other interesting birds that were around us.

It was just an hour after the hide had been apparently deserted that the hen buzzard arrived back. She perched on a branch a little way from the nest, carrying in her beak an oak twig with green leaves. For five minutes she remained there, looking about her, and then jumped to another branch above the nest. She dropped the oak twig and began to preen her neck and breast feathers, and as she did so, we saw for the first time at close range, something of the magnificence of her build and plumage. Her handsome proportions can best be judged by a glance at the photographs, but her colouring, alas, we have been unable to reproduce in this book. The general effect was of a rich chestnut brown in various shades, but each feather of her back and wings was beautifully graduated from a dark centre rib to a light edging, and her tail feathers were barred with fawn and chestnut. Her breast was marked with a large crescent-shaped patch of light feathers merging almost to white, and the effect was set off by the yellow legs and yellow beak with black tip. After about five minutes' preening she flew away through the wood. We were disappointed to see her go without alighting on the nest, but although she appeared to take no notice of the hide or camera lens, it may have been that she was a little suspicious. In another five minutes, however, she came back to the perch a little above and to the right of the nest, and almost at once flew down on to the back of the nest, facing the hide. The two chicks, both still covered in greyish-white down, stood up to greet her.

Picking up a stale rabbit which had been lying on one side, the hen fixed it under her left foot and began to pull it to pieces with her beak. First came fur, which she swallowed herself, but she quickly opened up the hind quarters, and gave the red meat to the larger of the two chicks. Her manner was fascinating to watch, for very tenderly and carefully, it seemed, she passed it with her beak, a little at a time, to the waiting chick. After ten minutes, the larger chick appeared to be satisfied and the smaller chick had his turn. His meal lasted nearly fifteen minutes, but the pieces given to him were distinctly smaller than those given to his elder brother. The hen then proceeded to pick up the fragments of rabbit that had been dropped in the nest, and swallowed these herself, but while she was doing this the large chick seemed hungry again and was given a further meal of rabbit.

During this meal we had an unexpected thrill, for the cock buzzard came down to the nest. There was no warning of his approach, and the hen merely gave a sudden glance round at his arrival. He remained in a fixed attitude while she continued to feed the large chick, and after three minutes left as suddenly as he had arrived. During his stay we had been able to compare the two birds, and noticed that although the rich chestnut colouring on the back and wings was similar in each, the breast markings were rather different, and the cock was generally rather lighter in colour about the neck and face. Another point of interest was that the hen had a fine sheen to her feathers whereas the wings of the cock were almost devoid of gloss. We conclude that the cock was probably a comparatively young bird and that his mate was a good deal older, a conclusion supported, in part, by the fact that her two eggs were nearly white, with only a few light fawn patches instead of the handsome reddish brown markings more characteristic of the buzzard.

The movements of the cock bird seemed scarcely to interest the hen, who ignored his departure and carried on feeding the large chick. The meals, in all, had lasted nearly forty minutes, after which, at 4.55 p.m., she began to feed herself. She tore off quite large pieces of rabbit and swallowed fur as well as flesh. Her meal lasted until 5.8 p.m., and was followed by a five minutes' doze on the side of the nest. The chicks had also gone to sleep and were now practically out of sight. After her doze, the hen spent a little while in tidying and decorating the nest. The remains of rabbit and other pieces were picked up and placed carefully round the edges, and the green oak twigs were pulled about and re-arranged until to her liking. It is certain they were used for purposes of decoration, but perhaps also as a garnishing or screen for the food store, because the leaves were often arranged to cover the meat and protect it from the sun and flies. At 5.27 she took her leave, launching herself over the edge of the nest and flying away between the tree trunks till she was lost to sight through the wood.

At 5.50 p.m. both birds returned together, the cock alighting in the middle of the nest and bringing a large rabbit with him, while the hen perched on a branch just below. They stayed, looking about them, for a little while, and we had an impression of their penetrating glances. The eye is fierce-looking, and the hooked beak adds to the air of ferocity, but already we had had a glimpse of how tender and appealing their manner could be, and even if it was perhaps partly sentiment, we could not help wishing to see the buzzard more adequately protected so that its breeding range could be re-established over a wider area.

We changed guard, as it were, shortly after six o'clock when a relief party came up to the hide. The hen buzzard listened anxiously to their approach as they came up the hillside, but remained quietly on the nest until, as they entered the wood, the cock, flying overhead, uttered his warning cry. She then launched herself over the side of the nest as she had done before, and flew away through the wood. We took the opportunity of examining the nest, and found a fresh fledgling blackbird in addition to the rabbit that had been brought during the afternoon. The young buzzards, at this stage, took little notice of us, but we soon climbed down from the nest and once again the relief party made its departure.

There was no sign of the adult birds for some time, but the chicks were very active and proved quite an engaging pair. They stood up periodically and stretched their wings, and the larger one made a determined attempt to preen himself. Although they were less than a fortnight old, they already showed clearly their hawk-like characteristics—the curved beak and the keen-looking eye—but they had a clownish appearance because, around each eye, was a narrow ring of down which was darker grey than that which covered the rest of their heads and bodies.

At 7.20 p.m. both adult birds came back through the wood together. They both alighted on a tree nearby, and then the hen came on to the edge of the nest. After standing for a few moments watching the chicks and looking about her, she began to feed them in much the same manner as before, using pieces of rabbit that had been lying on the side of the nest. The larger and more lusty chick was fed first with what seemed an enormous meal. He had, however, shown no signs of diminishing appetite when suddenly he turned away and crouched down into the nest, and the other chick took his place. We noticed no action on the part of the hen to indicate to the chick that he had had sufficient, and wondered what led to his sudden move, as a moment before, such a course had seemed most unlikely. Again the small chick was fed on noticeably smaller pieces of rabbit which were carefully selected by the hen. If a large piece came off the carcase she would put it down and pull at it again, and in the later stages when pieces of fur were coming off as well, she invariably ate those herself.

After her meal, the hen did a little digging with her beak in the bottom of the nest, and nosed the chicks about to get them where she wanted them. She then settled over them and began to preen herself lazily, and in a little while seemed to be half asleep. She was, however, always on the alert, and when the farmer shouted in the valley, or the dog at the farm barked, she instantly raised and turned her head in that direction. At 8.10 p.m. she left the nest, launching herself over the side in characteristic fashion, but she had been back three times by 8.25, each time bringing with her an oak twig with leaves. Two of the visits were quite short, and she only perched on the side of the nest and stayed long enough to arrange the foliage she had brought with her, but the third time, after she had finished her decorating, she stood for a while looking around her and especially upwards, as if wondering where her mate had gone. There was no sign of him, and she turned her attention to another short meal for the chicks. There followed a little more tidying of the nest, and then she settled down to brood them with her back to the hide. Her head was tucked right down and could not be seen, and as there was no further sign of movement, we could only presume that she had gone to sleep. There was a stillness in the wood and a silence, until at about 9 o'clock the relief party once more made its way to the hide, and we bade farewell to the buzzards after our first day in their company.

Our next visit to the buzzards was two days later, on 9th June. The weather was very unsettled, with thunderstorms and torrential rain at times, but there were brighter intervals which gave us some hope of photography. We had no extra helpers on this occasion, and one of us was installed in the hide, and the other made a lone departure at 2.45 p.m. The fact that only one person had left the vicinity, whereas two had previously arrived, did not seem to upset the buzzards, for at 3.20 the cock arrived back at the nest, bringing with him an oak twig. He perched on the front of the nest, but did not stay more than a few moments. At 3.30, both birds came back together, and the visit was the more interesting as the buzzards were being mobbed by jays. It was raining at the time, and the hen buzzard settled on to the nest and began to brood the chicks immediately. One of the jays perched on a branch close to the nest, but the buzzards took practically no notice of it, and when the chicks were safely sheltered under their mother, the cock buzzard flew away, drawing the jays after him. The rain continued heavily until 4.10, but conditions were not too insufferable in the hide as we had, fortunately, taken the precaution of tying the centre of our flat roof to a branch above, and so giving to it a slight angle which allowed some of the water to flow away. The buzzard was covered with large beads of water, and when the rain ceased, she left the nest. We noticed that the wet had made the chicks appear very much darker in colour, and they were quite a dull grey, but, on the back of his head, the larger chick had a diamond-shaped patch which had remained white.

Just after 5 o'clock we noticed the hen sitting on a tree not far from the nest, but she had not returned when there was some shouting at the bottom of the wood and she flew away again, and neither bird had put in any further appearance when we terminated our watch at half-past six.

The following day we began our observations at 2.25 p.m. The chicks appeared to be growing rapidly, and although

Tiny morsels from the rabbit were offered to the chicks
(Chicks 21 and 19 days old)

The meal over, the hen dragged the rabbit carcase to the edge of the
nest. (Chicks 21 and 19 days old)

Pl. 42

The hen buzzard with her back to the camera

Pl. 43.

At twenty-seven days the elder chick was well feathered on its wings

During a thunderstorm, the chicks scorned shelter, so the hen sat between them, and the rain bounced high off her back. (Chicks 36 and 34 days old)

Pl. 44

(Above) *One of the chicks engaged in wing-flapping exercise.* (*Chicks 38 and 36 days old*)

(Right) *The hide from which the buzzard photographs were taken*

Pl. 45

they were lying well down in the nest, they were holding up their heads and snapping occasionally at flies. The number of bluebottles that usually hung over the nest, attracted, no doubt, by the scraps of rabbit meat, was much reduced, but this was probably due to the showery weather, and the fact that only one hind quarter of rabbit remained on the edge of the nest, rather than to the activities of the young buzzards. The hen arrived back at the nest at 2.40 and stood for some three minutes looking about her and at the chicks. They stood up to greet her, but seemed a little impatient, and the larger one started pulling at the piece of rabbit that was on the side of the nest. She began to feed him on the rabbit, and as before, swallowed most of the fur herself, but on this occasion she was not so particular, and the chick occasionally had pieces of fur on his portions. He was given practically the whole of one rabbit leg, and then his younger brother was fed on a vole which the hen dragged up from the bottom of the nest. She seemed to have a special affection for the smaller chick, and although by now he appeared not far behind the other in the matter of development, yet her manner with him remained particularly delicate. She seemed to delight in tearing off small and tasty pieces of the vole and then, bending forward and with head turned on one side, she passed them gently to him with her beak. While this was going on, the larger chick helped himself to the remains of the rabbit leg, and tried, with just a little success, to pull pieces of meat off it. The meal finished at 3.1 p.m. and the hen immediately left the nest, dropping over the far side as usual, and gliding and flying away through the wood.

In two minutes she was back, bringing with her a large oak twig with about twenty leaves on it. She tried arranging it along the edge of the nest, having to pull several times at some of the leaves before it was to her liking. She then began to clean up the nest, eating small scraps from the bottom and re-arranging a few twigs here and there. The extreme care taken by this bird in maintaining the appearance and condition of her nest is, we believe, quite characteristic of the species. So long as she was not disturbed, her domestic duties followed a routine as clearly defined as that of many a housewife, and after her nest-cleaning and decoration was finished, her next act was to tidy herself. She began by preening a few of her own breast feathers, but soon gave her attention to the chicks, and each in turn was combed down the back with her beak. They were twisting their heads about and trying to preen themselves at the same time; but she was not bothered by this, and showed, rather, her satisfaction at the progress they were making. She certainly looked proud of them when, their toilet completed, she stood back on the edge of the nest and gazed at them for a few moments.

Having satisfied herself concerning their well-being, she once more gave thought to herself, and began by devoting a few minutes more to her breast feathers. She then preened her wings, and as each was lifted and spread in turn, we had magnificent glimpses of the beauty of line and colour embodied in them, and an impression of their enormous spread and power. Soon she settled to brood the chicks, preening herself spasmodically while doing so, but her siesta lasted less than half an hour, for at 3.36 p.m. she was disturbed by a carrion crow which croaked from a tree to the left of the hide. The hen rose to her feet, and both she and one of the chicks, who also stood up, stared across in the direction of the noise. While she was standing, we saw her mate flying overhead, but did not hear him call to her, but after a quarter of a minute she flew off, though we could not tell what action she took to deal with the crow.

She returned again in ten minutes, bringing another oak spray which was added to the nest, and then began to feed the chicks again on the remaining leg of rabbit. Both were fed at the same time on this occasion, having a piece each, more or less in turn, and we wondered whether this change of procedure was occasioned by the shortage of food on the nest. During this feed the buzzard was again disturbed, this time by some boys who passed noisily along the path at the bottom of the wood. She turned her head to one side and listened to them, and then, at the warning cry of her mate, she left the nest. The young ones were very active during her absence, moving about the nest a good deal, and standing up from time to time to flap wings, and although still covered in down, they showed promise of the wing power to come. It was pretty, on one occasion, to see them make an early attempt at preening each other, and as they turned about, we noticed that each now showed the white diamond-shaped patch on the back of his head, although their down was not yet as it was the other day, so presumably this marking develops during the growth of the down.

Neither adult bird put in an appearance for rather more than an hour, and then at 5.11 p.m. the hen arrived back, bringing with her a chicken. She stood on one side of the nest with her prey under one foot, and spent quite a few minutes tugging before she had it torn open sufficiently for feeding. We were interested to note, that although many of the birds that live on feathered prey have a plucking post at which they strip their victims before bringing them to the nest, the buzzard brought this chicken complete with all its feathers, and it strengthened our belief that feathered prey is rather unusual for the buzzard and is only taken if rabbit and other small mammals are difficult to obtain. The meal proceeded slowly, for, either the chicks were not hungry, in spite of the small amount they had eaten during the afternoon, or else they did not like the chicken, and they had taken very little, when, about half an hour later, we terminated our watch for the day.

Our next period of observation was the following afternoon, 11th June, when we arrived at the hide about 2.15 p.m. We climbed the tree to examine the nest and found the hindquarters of a full-grown rabbit in addition to the greater part of the chicken that had been brought the previous day, and there was an abundance of green twigs that had recently been added to the nest. Events followed much the same general course as they had on previous occasions, but during this spell we saw no sign of the cock bird. A field vole was brought to the nest during the afternoon, but the only food that was given to the chicks was from the rabbit, and we were interested to note that the chicken was not touched so long as other food was available. On 12th June we visited the nest and found a fresh decapitated rabbit, and on the 14th there was a half-grown rabbit on the nest when we arrived, and during a two-hour watch a small fledgling bird was brought and was swallowed whole by one of the chicks.

On 15th June, we spent another three and a half hours in the hide, and noticed for the first time that dead bracken was being used for nest decoration. The chicks seemed to be growing rapidly, and although still covered in grey down and showing clearly the white patch on the back of the head, the larger one had feathers beginning to show along the edges of his wings. The smaller chick had been playing for some time with the dead bracken when the hen arrived carrying another frond which she laid along the side of the nest. She picked up a rabbit, and after tearing at it for a few moments, began to feed the younger chick, who was whistling hungrily. After five minutes she turned her attention to the elder chick, and although the pieces offered to him seemed to be getting larger and larger, he was not given any fur at this time, but this may have been because there was plenty of meat on the rabbit. A few minutes later, the hen left the nest for some reason, but returned after a brief absence to continue the feed. This time the chicks were fed together, being given a piece each, alternately, and occasionally the hen took a large piece herself. When she had finished with the chicks, the hen continued to feed herself on large pieces of rabbit until there was very little left and then, after arranging the few remains round the edge of the nest, she took her leave.

We were unable to spend much time in the hide for a few days after this owing to exceptionally bad weather, but we examined the nest for food on the 17th and 19th of June. On the former occasion there was a half-grown rabbit, partly eaten, and, as usual, without head, and a fledgling blackbird that had not long been killed, while on our second visit there was a fresh field vole and two small rabbits complete with heads. On 21st June, we arrived at the hide at 12.25 p.m. with a few assistants and were soon left to our vigil. The larger chick was now well feathered on his wings and had traces of feathers on the upper part of the breast. He spent a considerable amount of time standing upright on the edge of the nest, and tried feeding himself off a fresh half-grown rabbit, but he was not very successful and pulled off rather more fur than meat. The smaller chick looked on enviously and whistled to be given some, but he made no attempt to feed himself and seemed at this stage to be lagging rather in development. He was only just beginning to show his wing feathers, and was still very shaky on his legs although he was now twenty-five days old and his brother twenty-seven.

At 1.50 p.m. both chicks were very restless and were indulging in wing-flapping exercises, holding on tightly to the nest as they did so, when their attention was drawn by a tree pipit scolding violently in the wood below them. They both moved to the edge of the nest, and in their efforts to watch the pipit they almost overbalanced. Soon, redstarts joined in the mobbing and a blackbird began to chuckle its alarm, and we wondered what could be disturbing the wood, when, at 2.5, the hen buzzard herself came back to the nest.

She stayed for about an hour, feeding the chicks for forty minutes and then having a short, but quite substantial meal herself. After re-arranging the remaining food round the nest, and picking her talons with her beak, she attempted to doze, standing on one leg and holding the other up under her breast feathers, but this attitude was not maintained for long, and she left the nest at 3.5 p.m.

Twenty-five minutes later, the quiet of the wood was again broken by the cries of angry green woodpeckers. Redstart and tree pipit joined in the outburst, and a jay voiced his annoyance with harsh cries. The disturbance moved nearer, and then seemed to centre on a tree a little to our left, and we soon saw that the buzzard was the cause of the demonstration. She flew from the mobbing throng and settled on a tree just to the left of the nest, being followed by a jay who nearly crashed into her as she sat perched. The jay went on, and alighted on a branch just above the buzzards' nest, but this proved too much for her and she jumped across, driving away the jay as she did so. It was remarkable how the mobbing ceased as soon as the buzzard was on her nest, and we recalled other instances, particularly at the nests of jay and tawny owl, where a fiercely mobbing throng of small birds has accompanied a predatory bird back to its nest, and then, seeming satisfied, has silently dispersed.

Almost immediately on her arrival, the hen buzzard perched on the sunward side of the nest and the elder chick moved round to the shade of her body, while the other sat in the sun by her. They made a delightful group, and we were pleased to find that they took no notice of the cine-camera which we were using on them for the first time. Half an hour passed with little activity to record except for casual spells of preening by the hen, when, at 4.5 p.m., they were again startled by some boys yodelling as they passed along the edge of the wood on their way home from the village school. The hen left hurriedly and had not returned by the time we left the hide at 6.15, although at 4.20 we had suspected her presence in the wood as there was another burst of mobbing in the distance, but this passed off without any sign of her.

At this stage of development of the chicks, we had planned to spend another full day in the hide and had selected 23rd June for the purpose, but the morning brought heavy rain which quite changed our inclinations. By the middle of the afternoon the weather cleared a little and we went up to the hide. We saw no sign of either buzzard as we climbed the hillside, but as soon as we entered the wood the cock bird called over our heads and the hen soon came into view, though we could not tell whether she came from the nest or not. The co-operation between this pair of birds was a source of continual wonder to us and it seemed quite impossible to surprise the hen on the nest.

On arrival we climbed the old oak and found the nest to be entirely devoid of food. There was a considerable amount of fresh twigs and leaves making the whole rim quite green, and the younger chick was picking at the oak leaves as if seeking something to eat. In a four-hour watch we saw no sign of either adult buzzard at the nest and concluded that they were having difficulty in finding food because of the wet weather. The chicks were making steady progress and both seemed more sure of their legs than on previous occasions. Their tail feathers were now quite noticeable, and the elder one was showing the characteristic crescent marking on his breast, although in his case it was composed of dark feathers whereas in the adults it was light. They were both quite active and walked about the nest and flapped wings while they were waiting, but every now and then they turned their heads skywards as if looking for their parents. We were interested to notice on one of these occasions when the young chick was standing on the edge of the nest, that a large bird swooped overhead and the chick ducked as if to hide or protect himself. Unfortunately we could not see the intruder but, from the cackling sound, judged it to be a magpie.

For about a week after this the weather was very unsettled with gales and torrential rain, and it seriously interfered with our observations. It may be thought that we should have been made of sterner stuff, but we felt discretion to be the better part of valour, and we contented ourselves with frequent visits to the nest to keep a check on the food supply. On 24th June there was an adult cock blackbird, and the following day there was no fresh food. On the 27th there was a half-grown rabbit and on the 28th a small rabbit, and it seemed that throughout this very wet spell the usual mammalian food of the buzzard was very difficult to obtain.

On 29th June it was still showery and threatening, but we decided to spend at least a little while with the buzzards, and arrived at the nest just after noon. The hide was standing up very well to the drenching and buffeting it was receiving, and we were glad to be inside it again. Our attention was taken at first by the chicks, who, in the last week, had grown almost beyond recognition. The elder one was covered in feathers, but the younger still had a good deal of down, especially on the head, and looked rather like a brown bird with a greyish-white head. We noticed that there was a chicken on the nest in addition to a half-grown rabbit and put it down to a serious shortage of other food. It was obvious that the weather conditions were having a very marked influence on the behaviour of the buzzards as well as on many of the other birds that we had under observation at the time. More than half of the ground-nesting birds were washed right out and lost their nests and families, and the wild life of the fields stirred but little on the rain-sodden ground.

The hen buzzard returned to the nest at 12.59 p.m. and began to feed the chicks. At first she gave to the smaller one a few morsels of the chicken, but he obviously disliked it, so she walked round the nest to the rabbit and used that for the greater part of the meal. When her offspring were satisfied, the hen, like a self-sacrificing mother, started to eat some of the chicken and left the rabbit remains in store. She was obviously hungry and we could not judge whether she herself had any real dislike of the chicken, although we recalled the previous occasion when rabbit was certainly eaten for preference.

Soon after her meal, the hen left the nest and all was quiet for a time, but about half-past one, the elder chick began to feed himself on the remains of rabbit. We were interested to notice that his method of plucking was now similar to that of his mother, and he fixed the prey under his left talons and steadied himself with his right foot while tearing at the rabbit with his beak. He succeeded in pulling off only small pieces of meat at a time, but persisted in his efforts for nearly an hour, and even a heavy shower of rain did not distract him. At 2.30 it rained in torrents and the water trickled and dripped from countless places in the hide. The chicks stood miserably in the nest and within a few minutes looked like two drowned rats. During the deluge, the hen arrived with a full-grown frog, but she just left it in the nest and did not stay. The cock paid a brief visit to the nest as if to see that the chicks were all right, and then, at 3.8 p.m., the hen came back again. The rain was now heavier than ever, and she stood in the middle of the nest and tried to encourage the chicks under her wings, but they seemed to be developing their independence and refused the shelter. At last she sat between them and the rain-drops bounced high off her back, and as she nestled there the chicks towered above her and looked almost as big as their mother.

At 3.25 p.m. the rain stopped suddenly and the hen soon left the nest to dry herself. She made no attempt to preen or dry the chicks as she had done when they were smaller, and they were left to fend for themselves. This did not bother them, and soon they were busy combing their feathers and flapping their wings, and we noticed that their wing span was now more than the width of the nest. Presently the sun broke through the clouds, and the chicks stood again and opened their wings to feel the warmth. Their flapping became very energetic and the larger chick actually lifted himself a little way off the nest. The exercise helped to dry the youngsters and soon they had regained their sleek appearance and the rain seemed quite forgotten. Before long the appetites quickened again and the elder chick seized the frog and, after several attempts, swallowed it whole, head first, while the younger chick hungrily picked about the nest in search of scraps. There was now, in fact, very little food left on the nest beyond a few remains of the chicken, and judging from the way the cock was returning periodically it seemed that he was having little success in catching anything.

Two days later we spent another period inside the hide and took the last of our photographs of the young buzzards on the nest. They were now rapidly developing the use of their wings and seemed almost ready for flight. In appearance they resembled their parents to a marked degree, although they still had considerable light markings on the head and face. Their appetites seemed enormous and a large part of the food was eaten soon after it was brought to the nest, so that at this stage we were unable to keep a complete check on what was consumed.

We visited the nest each day until the young birds left it, and noted with interest that although the quantity of green leaves was less now than it had been earlier, due no doubt to the less frequent visits of the parents, there still were some twigs newly added, and it seemed that the buzzards liked to preserve the fresh appearance of their nest to the very end. The elder chick left the nest on 6th July and the younger one four days later, so that the fledgling periods were 42 and 44 days respectively. In a sense we were sorry to find them gone, for they had been a fascinating study and we had developed a special regard for them, but it was good to know that they had safely passed the helpless nestling stage and could now rely on their own powers of flight. The sky was theirs, and the spread of the hills and valleys, beyond where the eye could see, but even as they entered on this new world, so they came at once to face perils far greater than nature had ordained for them. True it is that the conscience of man is stirring against the needless slaughter of our wild life, but the process is slow, and meantime the buzzard is in grave danger. He is a noble bird, worth preserving if only from an aesthetic point of view, but in point of fact he deserves more adequate protection than he now enjoys, for study reveals him to be economically useful in his preying on rabbits and voles, and his misdeeds, from the farmers' point of view, to be comparatively infrequent.

Chapter 9

DISCUSSION

IN every study, there must come, from time to time, a pause in the accumulation of fact and experience, an interval in which we can reflect on the work that has been done and reconsider the plans for the future. There must be a period for the correlation of the data that have been amassed, or much of the intrinsic value of the work will be lost through a failure to appreciate the full significance of the separate observations. It is to provide such an interlude, and to suggest lines of discussion and further study, that we include the few comments that make this chapter.

From time to time in the course of our watching, there have occurred incidents which have struck us as having some special significance in the study of bird life: incidents which have turned our thoughts to one or another of the many problems that confront the bird-watcher. Considered separately, they are of passing interest, but considered in relation to other observed facts, they help us to a more complete understanding of the bird mind.

One of the much discussed problems in ornithology is the existence of, or rather the extent of, intelligence among birds, and in the course of our work we have been constantly on the alert for evidence that would throw further light on this point. It will be realised, of course, that almost everything a bird does is to some extent relevant to this issue, but in the small space at our command, we can pick out from our observations only the outstanding incidents which suggest the capability for an ordered train of thought, which is the basis of intelligence. We adopt this line of approach since the existence of a faculty can be proved only by positive evidence. Negative evidence on this subject may suggest lack of intelligence, but does not prove it, since, in any particular instance the intelligence may be subservient to emotional or instinctive impulses. An experiment described by Mr. Kirkman in his book, *Bird Behaviour*, will serve as an excellent example of what we mean. He tells

how a black-headed gull returned to her nest and brooded a
tobacco tin which had been substituted for her eggs. At first
this might appear to be utterly stupid, but we must pause
to recollect that *homo sapiens*, at times of emotional stress,
may just as readily do things against the dictates of reason.

One of the earliest outstanding incidents that attracted
our attention to the bird mind, was the behaviour of the
pair of stone curlews in warding off the threatened attack
by a dog. The action of the hen in feigning injury to draw
the dog after her and away from the nest is a practice not
uncommon among birds, but the co-operation of cock and
hen and their obvious objective speech made us feel that
here was a pair of birds whose actions were far above the
levels of mere instinct. Now that the aspect of communication has broken into our consideration of intelligence, we
may as well perhaps recall some other instances where
communication of a higher order than the rudimentary alarm
notes has been observed between two or more birds, for
surely such "speech," if we may so call it, implies some
measure of intelligence. We recall that the stone curlews
afford us further examples in the conversation between cock
and hen during brooding and at the change-over, and that
with one pair that were kept under special observation, we
were able to associate definite sounds with certain actions
on the part of the birds.

Another good example of intelligent communication was
provided by the partridges we described in an earlier
chapter. It will be remembered that, at the time of hatching,
the hen left the nest and fetched the cock to help in the
task of drying the chicks, but how, unless there was intelli-
gible speech, did the cock know he was wanted? Except
at this particular brief period, and when escorting his mate
to and fro at feeding times, the cock partridge never comes
to the immediate vicinity of the nest, and it is hard to believe
that he could know by instinct of the arrival of his first-born.
Moreover, as we have mentioned previously, we noted
definite instances of conversation between the two parents
during the hatching of the family of partridges, and in
certain instances this "speech" appeared to be answered by
action on the part of one or other of the birds.

The partridges may be cited as providing yet another

Sandpiper and chick

*The woodcock is well matched to the dappled woodlands in which
she nests*

Pl. 46

*The marking of the ring plover blends with the lines and shadows of
her habitat*

The nightjar harmonizes perfectly with her surroundings

Pl. 47

aspect of intelligent action at the time when the family left the nest. In the ordinary course of events, their departure would have been a straightforward affair without any difficulties, but in this instance the hide blocked the obvious way out of the clearing in which the nest was situated, and the next obvious—and the one the hen had used on her travels to and from the nest—involved a climb up a bank that would have been difficult for the young chicks. The cock, therefore, pushed his way through the most suitable part of the surrounding undergrowth, and deliberately forced it apart with his wings so as to leave a sufficient and clear way for the hen and chicks. His action was very interesting to behold and caused us to reflect on the reasoning power of the bird when confronted with unusual circumstances.

The crow family are perhaps usually regarded as the most intelligent among British birds, and there is the interesting example of cunning recorded by Miss Frances Pitt in her book, *Animal Mind*, where she tells of the actions of two pet ravens in pilfering the food put down for the dog. One bird would distract the dog while the other robbed him, and the incident revealed a marked conspiracy and co-ordination of purpose. From birds in the field, we can produce no example quite so striking as that, but rooks have frequently given us a good deal of amusement as well as food for thought by their clever attempts to reach the fat hung out for the tits.

In addition to the regular bird table in the garden, we usually contrive one or more devices to exercise the acrobatic agility of the tit family, and of these attractions one of the most popular was a coconut shell cut in half and filled with meat fat, and suspended by string from a rustic screen. The tits accepted it and set to work within a few hours of its erection, and we looked forward to weeks of pleasure from so substantial an offering, but to our amazement, when we looked the following day, the shell was empty. Something had been at it before we were up and had made short work of the contents, so with a feeling of curiosity we replenished the bait and kept it under observation. There was not long to wait before a rook flew down to the screen and, reaching downward, seized the coconut shell in its beak and pulled it up on to the perch. Having succeeded so far he found no difficulty in wedging the shell under one foot while he pecked at the fat. We were delighted to see the rook at such close quarters, but at the same time were concerned at the speed with which he was disposing of the fat, so at a suitable opportunity we lengthened the string to about twelve inches to lower the coconut shell out of his reach. But in this we reckoned without the calculating mind of the rook. For some days the fat hung there immune from his covetous beak, and the tits swung and bobbed at their pleasure, but after a while the rook returned to the attack. He perched on the screen where the string was attached and, reaching downwards, seized the string with his beak. He drew it up, forming a loop which he held with one of his feet. He reached down again and drew up the string a little further, secured it again with a foot, and then in triumph reached down and seized the coconut. Whether he had previously attempted this feat in our absence we are unable to say, but he certainly succeeded at the first attempt that we saw, and we had to award him the honours for the best example of bird reasoning in our experience.

One feature of bird development that has attracted our attention and aroused our curiosity has been the extent of the period of incubation and its culminating phase—the period that elapses from the first sign of chipping of the egg-shell till the emergence of the chick—a period that we shall refer to as the "chipping time." For many quite common birds the incubation period is still only vaguely known, and we have been able to discover only very few references to observations on the chipping time. There are, of course, many difficulties in the way of obtaining this information accurately, but in those cases where we have been able to maintain a persistent watch, the results have had considerable interest. Most of our work in this direction has been devoted to the ground-nesting birds, that is, to those that have long incubation periods, and among them we have noted large variations of the chipping period and a tendency for the emergence of the chick to be influenced by weather conditions. One of the most re- markable examples of this was provided by a sandpiper, whose eggs were due to hatch, and indeed appeared to be on the point of hatching, on a certain day which turned out to be stormy. In the evening a severe thunderstorm broke with torrential rain, which washed out many of the smaller ground-nesting birds. The young sandpipers did not hatch that day, but remained safely inside their shells till the following morning, giving a chipping time of at least seventy-two hours, and we could not help feeling that it was more than a coincidence that the chicks escaped what must otherwise have been a considerable risk of death through drowning. There are numerous examples, many of them common knowledge, which suggest that birds frequently sense impending weather conditions, and, if we admit a measure of intelligence, it is not unreasonable to suppose that birds will, in some cases, adapt their behaviour to the prevailing or imminent conditions. In many cases, as we know only too well, birds are surprised or overtaken by unfavourable weather which thins their ranks by thousands, but it is in the individual instances of bird-conduct that we get our best glimpses of the working of the bird mind, and the evolution of those characteristics which assist in the preservation of the species.

The struggle for existence seems a very real thing for the majority of birds. They have their sportive moments, but the greater part of their time is given to the business of living. Like most wild creatures, they live in a state of continual anxiety for their own safety, and it is of interest to notice the conscious and the sub-conscious actions that result from this. The buzzards provided an excellent example of the alertness of eye and ear, and the co-operation between the cock and hen, without which the species would have been even more scarce in these islands than it is at present, and the wood pigeon showed her distrust of man and her anxiety to keep out of his sight. This necessity for concealment is one of the primary factors which influence the whole of a bird's life, and it forms a useful standpoint from which to consider the bird mind and bird development. For example, it is noteworthy that whereas many of the birds, such as the pied flycatcher and the grey wagtail, which are comparatively striking in appearance, nest in holes and other fairly well concealed places, many of the less conspicuous birds are content with less secure nesting sites. In ornithology, it is seldom wise to make general statements, but it is perhaps not too far from the truth to say that the optimum degree of inconspicuity is reached among the ground-nesting birds. These, by themselves, form an interesting study, for many of them reveal a remarkable correspondence between the marking of their own plumage and the nature of the particular situation favoured by them for nesting. The woodcock, as we have already mentioned, is heavily barred so that she is well matched to the dappled woodlands that are her home, while the snipe is more streaky in her marking and is well camouflaged among the grasses in which she nests. The stone curlew, by contrast, is only slightly flecked, but her sandy colouring makes her very inconspicuous among the open heaths which are her natural environment. The question immediately comes to mind as to whether these birds choose as their breeding places those situations which afford them the best natural camouflage, or whether, in the evolution of the species, the plumage has developed to conform with the birds' surroundings. There is perhaps some doubt about the former hypothesis, for the evidence available does not always suggest that birds appreciate the success or the failure of their plumage to match their environment, but on the other hand, it may be that because of the protection afforded by natural camouflage, there has been the greatest survival of those birds which have consciously or sub-consciously taken advantage of it, and their progeny have returned to breed in the type of situation in which they themselves were born, thus giving rise, in the case of those birds most prone to disturbance, to a relationship between plumage and habitat.

Already this discussion threatens to exceed the limits we planned for it, but it would indeed be conspicuously incomplete without a reference to the variations between birds of a species, and to the irregular distribution of certain species —points which have occurred several times in the course of the book—but particularly in connection with the grey wagtail and the pied flycatcher. In the case of some birds, such as the buzzard, obvious influences have controlled their distribution, while in other instances, of which the woodcock may be quoted as an example, consideration of feeding and nesting grounds give an answer to our queries, but so far we can find no solution to the problem of the distribution of the pied flycatcher. Many other birds are local, their range extending only part way across the British Isles, but often we can correlate their distribution with climatic and geographic features. The pied flycatcher appears in comparatively isolated communities in districts which seem to offer no unique attractions for the birds. The food is mainly insectivorous, but not unduly specialised, and many places where the bird is never found offer an abundant supply of food as well as nesting sites. Indeed, the pied flycatcher would seem to make little demands on the resources of a district, for, in those parts where it does nest, it appears to require very little territory, and many pairs may be found in a small area of garden or parkland. On the question of the marked difference between the arrival of the pied flycatchers in Wales and in Northern England, little can be added to what has already been said. Data of the birds' movements are required and this can only be obtained as a result of an intensive policy of ringing, but in the absence of knowledge on the subject, it seems not unreasonable to suggest that the Welsh birds and those from Northern England are two quite distinct communities, migrating separately and each returning year after year to the district in which, by some accident of Nature, the flocks were established.

The variations which result from an adaptation to circumstances are a study in themselves and offer a further valuable approach to bird mentality. Food supply, which is so important a factor in the lives of all living things, serves not unnaturally perhaps, to provide numerous examples of variation. Some birds, much more readily than others, seem able to vary their diet to correspond with the supplies of food available, and it is noteworthy that such species show a marked ability to maintain their stock even in the face of unfavourable weather conditions. Variations of nesting site, and of habit and manner between birds of a species, all offer interesting and maybe instructive lines of research, and these are but a few drops, as it were, in the ocean of ornithology.

Any review that we can make, may serve in some measure to indicate the next few steps to be taken in our pursuit of knowledge, but as in all sciences, it shows us how little we really understand. The field for new observations and for research is limitless, but the advancement of knowledge can be assisted by small discoveries, as well as by investigations of major importance, and if any of the facts that we have set down, or any of the ideas we have expressed, may lead to a wider interest in bird watching and through that to a deeper understanding of life, we shall have achieved one of our objectives in this book.

Chapter 10

THE APPROACH TO BIRD-PHOTOGRAPHY

IN some of the foregoing chapters we have referred briefly to the erection of hides and to other details of the preparation involved by our studies, and readers will, no doubt, have deduced something of the methods of the bird-photographer. It may be, however, that some would like to know more about how we come to grips with our avian quarries, for, in the course of writing and lecturing about birds, we have found that the telling of our story often arouses considerable interest in our work as distinct from our results; over and over again we are asked how we manage to get such photographs as those reproduced in this book, and so we include this and the next chapter, which we hope will prove both interesting and instructive.

Although we describe our own methods, we do not wish to give the impression that ours is the only way of achieving the results, and we do not claim that our technique has reached the limit of perfection, but our own is obviously the way we are best qualified to describe. In general, the methods of most bird-photographers are similar; they aim at concealing themselves close to some known rendezvous of their quarry, whether it be a nest, a drinking pool or even a favourite perch; but the details by which the result is achieved vary as widely as the tastes of man. In the beginning we based our work on the methods of some of the pioneers of bird-photography, and received valuable advice from our friend, Ian M. Thomson, and from that foundation we have built up by experience a technique of our own. Similarly now, others may like to have the benefit of our experience, and we gladly pass on some of the things that we have learned.

Right at the start of this chapter we must make it clear that our preparations are nearly always governed by photographic considerations, and this fact should be borne in mind by those who, though not photographers, would like to watch birds at close quarters, to see some of the things that we have seen, and to make fresh observations of their own. No one should feel discouraged from bird-watching because he is not a photographer, for the camera is not at all essential to the bird-watcher, and while there is undoubtedly some value in the photographic record and no little satisfaction in the production of a good bird photograph, it should be realised that the manipulation of a camera is often a hindrance to the more important business of recording in detail the incidents that are being observed. The demands of the camera are more exacting than the demands of the eye, so that in any case photography is possible only during relatively limited periods compared with the time available for observation, and these same limitations of the camera always involve a restricted disposition of the hide, and often lead to difficulties in its construction. The non-photographer can work successfully from the hides that we shall describe, but he will find, by experience, that in many cases he can observe adequately without being quite so close to the bird, and that by so doing he can take more liberties in the arrangement of the hide and so simplify its erection.

Like any other enterprise, bird-photography needs a certain amount of planning if it is to be carried through expeditiously, and we propose accordingly to suggest something of the plans and preparations we make before we leave home for a season's work. The time at our command controls to a large extent the scope of our activities, and we must obviously so frame our plans that we utilise the precious hours to the best advantage. If evenings and week-ends were our only opportunities for bird-watching, we should of necessity arrange to work as close as possible to our homes so that the minimum of time would be spent in travelling. The species we could observe would probably be somewhat restricted, but still vast possibilities for study would be open to us. In this chapter, however, in order to show what are perhaps more nearly ideal arrangements, we are thinking of those favourable conditions when we have been able to devote the greater part of the spring and early summer to bird-photography. We refer to this as the "bird season" because it is definitely the season of greatest activity among the birds and conditions are usually favourable to

A typical tree hide, built to photograph a kestrel

Pl. 48

One of our "standard" hides with the covering removed to show the construction

Pl. 49

photography, but bird-watching and photography are not limited to these few months, and as opportunities occur, the study is continued throughout the year.

We choose, as a rule, some particular locality for a season's work, studying in particular the birds which are special to that district, but extending our observations to cover all the local birds as far as possible. Thus, in Suffolk we may concentrate on the stone curlew, but in Wales the grey wagtail and the pied flycatcher may take our special attention. As early as possible in the year we make a preliminary trip to our selected hunting-ground to get some idea of the local conditions, and we take the opportunity to arrange for lodgings and ascertain the local facilities for the development of photographic plates and films. This may seem a relatively trivial item, but it is, in fact, of the utmost importance and the success of a season's work may depend on the arrangements we make. Bird-watching can make big demands on the physique, especially if the country is at all rugged, and when one considers the necessity, on occasions, of being up with the lark, and at other times of working into the night in quest of the nocturnal creatures, one realises the advantages to be gained by staying with people who are at least sympathetic in a practical sort of way. The problem of the development of films when away from home is one that is shirked by some people, but from bitter experience we have learned the advisability of checking our photographic results as quickly as possible, and we make a point of developing our negatives while there is still a possibility of repeating them if necessary. Photographic materials reach a high standard of reliability nowadays, but even so, they have failed us on occasions, and even the most robust apparatus is not immune from the possibility of trouble.

We have always been very kindly received by the owners of the estates on which we have worked, and the facilities they have accorded us have contributed in no small measure to the achievement of our results. One privilege that has often been of the greatest help to us has been the assistance of the gamekeepers and wardens, for, with their detailed knowledge of the ground and its denizens, these men have been able to give us valuable advice and have often saved us hours in the search for some particular nesting site. It so happens that the spring is one of the busiest seasons of the year for a gamekeeper, and he will have little time to devote to a mere bird-photographer, but one of the best ways of getting to know the ground and its possibilities is to accompany the gamekeeper when he is "going his rounds," and we make a point of doing this during our preliminary trip. In this way, we not only get a good knowledge of the extent of the estate where we have permission to work, but we quickly learn the likely haunts of the various species that are known to nest in the locality, and, perhaps more valuable still, we get to know the various tenant farmers and other workers on the estate, for their co-operation and goodwill have an important bearing on our prospects.

From our brief preliminary survey, we return with a fair idea of the work we hope to do during the season, and we begin our detailed preparations, paying special attention to the species that are to be the primary objectives in our chosen locality. Quite apart from any consideration of equipment, there is one important preparation that should not be overlooked, and that is a certain amount of reading. In any scientific study, one of the essential preliminaries is a knowledge of the work done by other investigators in the same field, and no bird-watcher can afford to ignore the results of other people's observations on the species he is watching.

Turning to the problem of equipment, we suggest that the most essential items to every bird-watcher are a note-book and pencil. The need for careful and systematic records cannot be too strongly emphasised, and from a considerable experience of bird-watching, we find it quite unsafe to rely on memory for more than a few minutes during periods of even moderate activity at a nest. General impressions certainly do remain, but the detailed facts of habits and feeding become a jumbled mental picture of no scientific value, unless they are jotted down at the time they occur. We find that the most satisfactory way of keeping our records complete and easy for reference is to use an indexed loose-leaf note-book and to classify the notes according to species, but care must be taken in every case to see that the relevant features such as time, locality and weather conditions are not omitted. In order that note-taking shall not be too laborious a business and thereby suffer neglect, it is worth while to formulate in advance some definite system of recording that will reduce the time occupied in writing, and at the same time will help to ensure that none of the essential features is missed. There is not the space in this book to enlarge on our own methods, but very little experience will indicate to anyone the lines on which he can develop a system to suit himself, while valuable guidance on the subject can be found in E. M. Nicholson's book, *The Art of Bird Watching*.

The other piece of apparatus that is almost indispensable to all bird-watchers is a good pair of binoculars. In general we have to locate birds and watch them from a distance before we can observe them closely from a hide, and even if this latter is our ultimate aim, there is much to be learned from distant watching, and we should not neglect to observe birds in flight, and their activities away from the nest. Much could be written concerning the various features that, from the point of view of the bird-watcher, are desirable in binoculars.

The choice is, perhaps, largely a matter of taste, but we demand before all else, a large field of view, since this facilitates the observation of birds in rapid flight, and is of considerable benefit when both birds of a pair are sitting a little way apart and it is desired to keep watch on both of them. We favour a linear magnification of about seven or eight times with standard binoculars, or up to ten times with the lightweight models, as we find this the limit that we can hold steadily for any length of time, but there are occasions, such as when watching a bird perched at a con-siderable distance, when we prefer much greater magnifica-tion, and for this purpose an additional piece of equipment in the form of a telescope is very useful.

The details of the photographic equipment cannot be dealt with in this brief account of our preparations. Let it suffice for now to say that we carry several cameras for taking both still and moving pictures, and a supply of film for colour as well as monochrome results. The apparatus must, of course, be in thoroughly good order, and occasional checking and overhaul is advisable to minimise the risk of breakdown in the field. Sometimes modifications and additions seem desirable for certain purposes, and these are put in hand in good time for them to be thoroughly tested before we leave home.

The provision of suitable hides is often one of the most formidable tasks that confront the bird-watcher, but we have found that it is certainly one that well repays the time and trouble spent on it. It is, without doubt, quite possible to engage in bird-photography from hides and shelters improvised in the field, but such a course is uneconomic; it is usually rather unsatisfactory, and it is open to several serious objections which will be self-evident when we consider the desirable attributes of a hide. Primarily, of course, the hide must afford us a sufficient view of the bird we wish to study, and must screen us from the perception of our quarry, but as we have mentioned elsewhere, it should, as far as possible, be sufficiently roomy to accommodate an observer with reasonable comfort for long periods. From practical considerations it should, in general, be easily and quickly erected and dismantled, and should be readily portable over difficult country. It should be durable, and able to stand for considerable periods against the destructive influence of rain and gales without breaking down or loosening in any way that might distress a bird nesting close to it; finally, it should be adaptable to suit various situations and conditions. It will be obvious that one type of hide cannot serve for every circumstance that we meet, but we have found it possible to standardise our hides to some extent to minimise the material and labour required for their construction.

In preparation for a season's work, we make about eight hides, each about three feet square. A few are short, that is, about four feet high, but the majority stand six feet. All are similar in construction and consist of four jointed poles, connected at the tops by stiff wires, and having a covering of fabric. The general arrangement is best understood by reference to the photograph (Plate 49). We usually carry a mallet in the equipment so that the framework of the hide can be driven sufficiently into the ground to ensure rigidity, and by the same means the height of the hide can be controlled within limits to suit each particular situation. The fabric should preferably be rather drab-coloured to render the hide as inconspicuous as possible, and it should be sufficiently thick to make the hide quite opaque even when viewed against the sun. Many hides will, at some part of the day, come between the bird and the direction of the sun, and the watcher can work with confidence only if he is sure that the bird is not able to discern a shadowy form moving behind the screen that has been erected so close to its nest. After the principal requirements have been met, there are one or two other features of the fabric that should be considered. The hide is sure to be subject to most kinds of weather, and it will add to the comfort of the occupant if the material is closely woven so that it will resist a certain amount of rain, and it should be mechanically strong enough to withstand being pinned tightly round the frame so that no loose edges can flap should the wind become boisterous. Finally, it is worth choosing a dye that is reasonably resistant to fading, for even in one English summer it is surprising how some hides tend to bleach, and such deterioration, of course, renders them too translucent for many situations.

Beyond the provision of these standard hides, which serve for the observation of birds which nest within five or six feet of the ground, we always make some preparation for the erection of tree-top hides, and for lofty structures such as we illustrate at the nest of the Kestrel. These hides must always be built to suit individual requirements, and while we usually arrange for a local supply of timber, we take a roll of hessian for the covering, and a quantity of assorted nails and tacks and several lengths of rope. Wire netting is a useful adjunct for a tree-top hide and can often be used to increase the rigidity of the structure as well as to support a camouflaging screen of leaves and branches, but we do not use it regularly and so rely on obtaining a roll locally if we need it.

The construction of these special hides will be dealt with in the next chapter when we refer to preparations in the field, but before we consider that stage of the work, we must mention a few other miscellaneous items that will add to the comfort or convenience of the bird-watcher who

8

includes them in his outfit. In particular, we advise a pair
of rubber boots. In many parts of the country marshland
is encountered and is found to be a favourite nesting and
feeding ground for numerous species, while frequently we
have had to work in streams and dykes in search of the
warblers and the water-loving birds. A small folding-stool
is a most useful piece of equipment on many occasions,
both outside, and especially inside, the hide, but if it is to
be used close to any of the larger and more timid birds it
should be thoroughly tested for comfort, since a stool of
unsuitable height can cause severe cramp during the long
periods of enforced fixed attitude. These rather exacting
demands of bird-watching call for some special thought in
the matter of clothing. It must be adaptable to suit extremes of activity from immobility to strenuous walking
and climbing, and extremes of temperature from hot sun
to night frosts, and while it should afford some protection
against the thorns of bramble and hawthorn, it must be
loose-fitting enough not to cause discomfort during spells
of motionless crouching. An ample supply of pockets is a
valuable feature, and one should be large enough to accommodate the note-book, so that it is always handy and ready
for use. We must, of course, have adequate protection
against rain, and find an oilskin hat very useful, since it
takes no extra height in a hide and is readily folded into a
pocket when not in use. And so, equipped from head to
foot against the vagaries of the weather, and supplied with
the needs of our craft, we load the car and set forth in early
spring for what always proves to be a real adventure. Our
destination is known, it is true, but we never know at the
beginning of a season just what we shall see and what we
shall be called upon to do, and the thrill and fascination of
bird-watching lures us again and again to the quiet, un-
molested tracts where time matters little, and the days
are measured by the waking and roosting of the feathered
throng.

Chapter 11

FIELD WORK

"CIRCUMSTANCES alter cases," is a well-worn phrase, but it is, none the less, particularly true when applied to the study of bird life, and a method of working that may be eminently successful at one time may fail to achieve the desired result on another occasion. In consequence of this, we must begin this chapter by emphasising that the methods we describe are those that we have found successful in the circumstances in which they were applied. They may frequently succeed again, but the bird-watcher must always use discretion and profit by his own experience, modifying his approach to his quarry according to the needs of the moment.

Quite naturally, one of our first tasks, on arrival in a district, is to locate a few suitable nests. The local people, especially keepers and farmers, are often of considerable help in this connection, particularly when we are working on a bird that affects their interests. They know at least the approximate situation of many of the nests of the birds of prey in their neighbourhood, and from their thorough knowledge of the ground and their constant watching, they know the favoured haunts of some of the other birds which concern them less directly. It was a casual remark of a farmer that led to our discovery of the little owl's nest in the old building. He had seen the owls about in the vicinity, and there his interest ended, but his observation gave us the clue that resulted in our series of pictures.

There are several ways of finding the nests we wish to observe, and the procedure in each case depends partly on the species concerned, and partly on the nature of the country. A previous knowledge of some of the habits of the birds is a valuable asset, as it helps us to avoid being deceived by the bird under observation, for many of them display mannerisms which protect the nest by misleading the unwary intruder. The most general form of this is the habit, common to the majority of ground-nesting birds, of alighting some little distance from the nest and walking the remaining distance through the shelter of the grass or herbage. The skylark and the tree pipit may be cited as examples of species with this characteristic, and indeed, the nest of the latter is frequently so well concealed among heather or grass that it is extremely difficult to locate it, even if we do know that the bird has alighted in its vicinity. Such nests are most frequently found by the expedient of watching carefully ahead of us as we tramp across likely haunts of these birds, and noting the exact spot from which a sitting bird has flown.

In the case of the larger and more timid birds, such as the redshank, which nests on marshes and salt-flats, a modification of this "putting-up" method is often necessary as the birds rise from their nests when we are still a long way off, and it is difficult to estimate, with any exactitude, the point from which a bird has risen. With these birds, having established the approximate position of a nest, we retire for a while to let the wild life re-settle on the marsh and later, re-approach stealthily, keeping cover behind a dyke or some natural screening. Two of us take up positions some distance apart, and then, at a given signal, emerge together into the view of the sitting bird. As she rises from the nest we each note the bearing in relation to suitable fixed points on the ground and walk in the directions we have determined. If our eyesight is keen and our course true, we shall converge at the nest itself, but in any case our error of judgment should be insufficient to lead to much trouble in discovering its exact location. A point to bear in mind in using this manœuvre is that many birds, in leaving the nest, walk or run a short distance before taking to the air, and it is, in consequence, necessary to watch very closely for the first sign of movement.

The nests of many of the small birds that build in hedge-row and scrub are often best found by the exercise of considerable self-restraint. It is true that we do sometimes find nests by determined searching, but how often it is more profitable, and at the same time more interesting, to stand back in some sheltered spot while the birds reveal their own secrets. It was a fine warm day when we were sitting in the shade of a hedge bordering an expanse of heath land. The ground was covered for the most part with a short, but dense, crop of heather, and here and there were clumps of gorse brightening the scene with a brave show of golden blossom. The air seemed full of small birds flitting to and fro and revelling in the sunshine of early summer, and as we sat, quiet and motionless, some approached and continued their busy toiling within a few feet of us. Among the twittering throng, a pair of whinchats took our special attention. We noticed them working regularly in a restricted area, and returning again and again to one particular stem of gorse, from which they dropped down out of our sight behind the screen of heather. With the aid of our binoculars we could see that they were carrying nesting material when they arrived on the favoured perch, and, concluding that they were building in its vicinity, we made a note of the position to inspect it at a later stage. Several other nests were discovered during that same period of watching, and although to the uninitiated the method may appear to be slow, we actually saw far more than we should have done had we blundered into the open and disturbed the wild life around us.

Interesting events, as well as nests that may be suitable for working, are not infrequently noticed, more by chance than anything else, provided we keep a sharp watch around us as we pass to and fro about the countryside. We recall one such incident near the edge of a wood in Suffolk where we were walking one June morning. We were out with the gamekeeper, and the three of us kept in single file as we wound our way through the rapidly growing bracken. The wood was not dense, for it consisted mainly of well-grown but well-spaced oaks, and for undergrowth there was nothing but the fresh green bracken, then about three feet high.

The keeper was the first to notice a disturbance among the birds away on our left, and, ever on the alert for his enemies, the stoat and weasel and the birds of prey, he quickly changed his course to seek the cause of the trouble. It was not long before his experienced eye fixed its gaze on an old dead stump—such a stump as a woodpecker might use for its nest—and, as he approached it cautiously, away flew a full-grown jay. We gathered at the nesting hole, for, yes, it had been the nest of a lesser spotted woodpecker; but the jay had been busy. The nest was in a very sorry state, the wall having been broken completely away below the entrance hole, leaving a cavity so shallow that the attacking bird could easily reach the baby woodpeckers. Fortunately, we had come in time to disturb the invader before he had finished his work of slaughter. Two of the birds were still in the hole and, so far as we could see, were unharmed, so the friendly keeper decided to save them if possible. He replaced the fragment of wall that had been torn out by the jay, and for further protection covered it with a piece of bark and bound the whole firmly with string. The nest certainly looked odd, but we hoped the parent woodpeckers would forgive the looks, and we retired to a distance, where, from the shade of an oak, we were able to watch the old birds return to feed what remained of their family.

It would be an easy matter to go on for a long time with interesting incidents that have come our way in the course of nest finding, and only the necessity for keeping this book within reasonable limits prevents us from enlarging on some of the delightful and thrilling occasions when we have come unexpectedly face to face, as it were, with some new aspect of bird life. But as we cast our thoughts across the whole extent of the subject, one salient principle dominates all else. On the vast majority of occasions, we have succeeded by the exercise of patience and self-restraint. Bold, open and aggressive methods of bird-watching are often slow in the long run, and defeat their own ends by disturbing the very beings we wish to study, and whether our quarry be the elusive short-eared owl on a Norfolk marsh, or the ubiquitous robin in a roadside bank, we usually achieve our best results by quiet and unobtrusive watching.

After a few days of preparation and exploratory wanderings, we shall almost certainly have selected a few nests which interest us and which, at the same time, are in reasonable situations from the points of view of observation and photography. Some of them may require the construction of special hides, but others are sure to be on or near the ground, in positions such that we can use our standard hides, and these are dealt with first, as the hides are easily and quickly erected and will give us an opportunity of beginning our close-up observations. Two or three such hides are set up, as, although it will not be possible to use them all at once, it is not at all unlikely that one or more of the nests will come to grief in the ceaseless struggle for existence between birds and their enemies.

One of these hides was set up at the nest of the snipe referred to previously. The nest was on a tussock in swampy ground to which cattle had access, and we had accordingly, in addition to the usual precautions, to take suitable steps to safeguard the nest and hide from their inquisitive attentions. As usual, we did most of our preparatory work at dusk, and after due consideration had been given to the best viewpoint, both as regards lighting, and the probable course of the bird in approaching the nest, we erected the hide, temporarily, at a distance of about twelve or fifteen feet. A wire fence was put up to prevent the cattle from trampling around the hide and on the snipe's eggs, and we then left the marsh as quickly as possible to allow the snipes to return and accustom themselves to the new erection in the vicinity of their nest. An evening or two later, we returned and re-erected the hide in the position from which we intended to work. The front was then only some five or six feet from the nest, but the structure was securely driven into the ground and the covering firmly fastened to prevent any movement, and there was little doubt that the birds would disregard it entirely. To reduce the change in appearance that would be involved when the camera lens was put into position in the front of the hide, an old bottle was tied in its place, and the hide was left until we were ready and able to use it.

A garden warbler nesting in a bramble was the objective in the case of another of these small hides. In this instance the screening of foliage made it unnecessary for the hide to be erected at a distance before it was placed in position, but here, as in most cases, the preparations were spread over a period of two or more days, the subsequent work taking the form of "gardening", or arrangement of the foliage protruding between the nest and the camera. A large stem of bramble that passed close in front of the hide had to be pulled to one side out of the field of view, as it would have been badly out of focus, and a few smaller pieces were tucked out of the way, but the immediate screening and cover to the nest was left in place right up to the time that we began our observations, as without this the birds would have been unnecessarily exposed to the sun and weather, and to observation from their enemies. Those small stems that had to be disturbed to enable us to see the nest, were not cut off, but were fastened back in such a manner that they were readily replaced between each spell of watching. A point to remember in this connection is that shadows cast by the sun change their direction in the course of the day, and that it is insufficient to notice that the chicks are sheltered from the sun at the moment we leave them. A case came to our notice where a family of young chaffinches were scorched to death through a lack of realisation of this point, and we hope that this instance may serve as a reminder to any who may not have foreseen the distress that can be caused by uncovering a nest.

A good deal of the procedure involved in getting into a hide, and in the subsequent vigil, has already been referred to in the course of earlier chapters, and need not be repeated here, but we may perhaps, with advantage, summarise a few points which occur to us as the result of our experiences. The note-book and pencil, and the stool, should not be left behind under any circumstances, and as regards clothing, it is as well to treat all the weather conditions as if they were extreme. Thus, an hour or two of sitting in a hide can make a chilly day seem bitter, and a warm day, swelter-ing, and if the ground is inclined to be boggy, the continual pressure and trampling in one place will bring a surprising amount of water to the surface, so that rubber boots, for preference, should be worn in damp places.

Once we are installed in a hide, the greater part of our attention is usually centred on the nest in front of us, but a good deal of interest is to be found in watching the coming and going of our quarry, and in noticing the activities of the other creatures that busy themselves around us. For this reason it is as well to make a small peephole in the back and in each side of the hide, but such holes must not be much more than mere slits, or the opacity of the hide will be affected.

The redshank's nest on the marsh

The redshank settles to brood her eggs

Pl. 50

The skylark (above) *and the tree pipit* (below). *Such nests are frequently found by watching ahead of us as we tramp likely haunts of these birds*

Pl. 51

The lesser spotted woodpecker returns to the mended nest

A garden warbler nesting in a bramble

Pl. 52

The hen green woodpecker

A pylon hide erected to photograph the green woodpecker

Pl. 53

An interesting example of the use of such a spy-hole occurred once when we were watching a hedge sparrow. The hide was fairly well hemmed in by the thick undergrowth in which the nest was situated, and in the quiet of the forest clearing, we seemed remote from all activity except for the regular visits of the parent hedge sparrows. Suddenly, quite close to us, there sounded a tapping noise. It was repeated, and then, peering carefully through the small slit in the side of our hide, we saw a little wren perched on a wooden stump within a couple of feet of us. In his beak was a green caterpillar almost half his own length, and he was holding it by one end and flogging it to death on the stump. It was one of those sights that stick in a bird-watcher's memory, and it impressed on us the value of side peepholes in even the most unpromising situations.

As we mentioned in the previous chapter, the birds that nest in the tree-tops, and in other situations much above ground-level, give us a good deal more trouble in the preparation of hides, since in these cases each hide must be constructed on the spot, and adapted to suit the particular local conditions. Where possible, as it was in the case of the buzzard and the kestrel, we use the neighbouring trees, or even the one in which the nest is built, to serve as the support for our hide, and nail the platform securely to suitable boughs. In such cases it will often be necessary to make the platform triangular, or of an irregular shape, but whatever form is finally evolved, care must be taken to incorporate sufficient ties or bracing, so that the main boughs used as supports shall not sway independently in a breeze. Furthermore, if the hide is to be used for photography, it is often desirable to brace the hide to the bough carrying the nest, so that there shall be no large relative movements which would upset the focusing of the camera. In work of this kind, the services of the local woodman will be found invaluable, and we gladly acknowledge the assistance that has been given us on many occasions.

One of the greatest difficulties in the construction of tree-top hides lies in getting the hide in a suitable position, and it is comparatively few trees which afford us the ideal viewpoint as regards direction, height, and distance from nest.

Accordingly, we often need to build what are almost watch-towers, as we did in the case of the green woodpecker. The construction of this hide is self-evident from the photograph, and is typical of many that we have used and found very satisfactory. Such a hide, and this also applies to those built in the trees, must be built by easy stages, so as to avoid sudden changes in the surroundings of the nest, and the work is usually spread over at least a week, and often takes longer.

A question that often arises is, "What is the most satisfactory time for the erection of a hide?" but it is one that allows no simple definite answer. In general, it may be said that the period when a bird is least likely to show concern is during the later stages of incubation, and in the case of timid birds it is perhaps best to restrict the commencement of activities to this period. In special circumstances, such as we encountered in our work on the buzzard, it may be necessary, because of extraneous influences, to defer operations until the eggs are hatched, while in the case of many of the smaller and less timid birds, the hide may be erected at almost any time after incubation has begun, provided reasonable precautions are taken. Not infrequently, however, the hide must be in position in time to achieve a given object, which may be, for example, an observation of the brooding habits of a pair of birds, and in such cases we must proceed with due caution, in the realisation that the birds are the more liable to be upset at this time by undue interference on our part.

Having now found a few nests and erected our hides, we enter on one of the most instructive and fascinating phases of bird-watching. Our outline plans will, of course, have been made long ago, but though there may be special features we intend to study we must be prepared, like true pioneers and investigators, to accept and record whatever events come under our notice, and to adapt our watching to the needs of the moment. The detailed plans must, therefore, be made from day to day, and it would, accordingly, be futile to describe here anything but the broadest of outlines on which we work.

In all cases, except perhaps in the course of some special experiment, one of our primary cares must be to ensure that the bird under observation is allowed to behave naturally, and to this end all our actions must be planned. Everything that will help to allay the birds' suspicions concerning the hide is well worth the trouble it may cause us, and in all our activities near the nest our first consideration must be the birds themselves. Observations made without due attention to this point may be entertaining, but from the scientific point of view, they will be worthless as representing the normal activities of our quarry.

If we can arrange to enter our hide during a period when the birds are away from the nest, so much the better, but even then it is advisable to have an escort who will leave us hidden and, by his departure, will quieten the misgivings of the wild life in the neighbourhood. Once in the hide, we proceed with considerable caution. "Familiarity breeds contempt," seems to be equally applicable among birds as among the humans of which it was written, and we find that if only we begin our watching with special care and avoid arousing the suspicions of our quarry in the early stages, most birds will readily accustom themselves to, and ignore, the sundry slight noises that are almost inevitable in the course of photography.

The variations of habit among birds are often so great that each must be treated as an individual, and we must avoid the pitfall of assuming that, because a bird belongs to a particular species, it will respond to a given set of circumstances according to a fixed code. It is this individuality among birds that makes their study so absorbing, and it is for this reason that we spend as much time as possible at each nest where we erect a hide. The same fact leads us to study pair after pair of the same species, and we can safely say that no repetition of a set of observations has ever been devoid of interest and value.

INDEX

(Figures in italics refer to Plates)